HOW THE WORLD WORKS
THE UNIVERSE

HOW THE WORLD WORKS
THE UNIVERSE

*From the Big Bang to the
present day... and beyond*

Anne Rooney

ARCTURUS

This edition published in 2019 by Arcturus Publishing Limited
26/27 Bickels Yard, 151–153 Bermondsey Street,
London SE1 3HA

Copyright © Arcturus Holdings Limited
Anne Rooney has asserted her right to be identified as author of this
work under the Copyright, Designs and Patents Act 1988

All rights reserved. No part of this publication may be reproduced,
stored in a retrieval system, or transmitted, in any form or by any means,
electronic, mechanical, photocopying, recording or otherwise, without
prior written permission in accordance with the provisions of the
Copyright Act 1956 (as amended). Any person or persons who do any
unauthorised act in relation to this publication may be liable to criminal
prosecution and civil claims for damages.

ISBN: 978-1-78828-634-3
AD006065UK

Printed in China

CONTENTS

Introduction:
IN THE BEGINNING...

'The Universe is not only queerer than we suppose, it is queerer than we can suppose.'

Mark Twain (1835–1910)

Understanding the universe is the greatest of all possible challenges and has occupied humankind from the earliest times. The questions 'What is all this?' and 'Where did all this come from?' are among the most fundamental we can ask.

Creation and cosmology

For millennia, the only way of approaching such questions was through religion, myth and story, none of which encourages exploration or interrogation. Creation myths are passed on from generation to generation; their stability is part of their essence and appeal. If you grow up in a culture which teaches, like the Kuba people of central Africa, that the stars were vomited up by a giant called Mbombo you don't need to look further for an explanation. Asking 'where did Mbombo come from?' might be thought at best silly and at worst heretical. Science, on the other hand, seeks to discover the truth even at the cost of overturning its most cherished

A 17th-century depiction of a Hindu origins myth, in which the universe is destroyed and created afresh in an endless cycle. Between acts of destruction and creation, Vishnu rests on the serpent Ananta, which represents eternity.

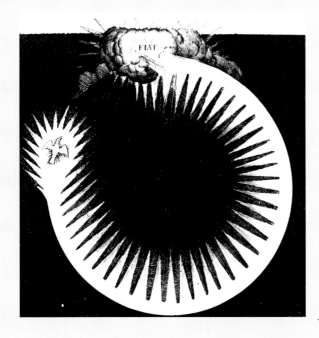

In Christian tradition, everything is created from God's word. Robert Fludd's Utriusque cosmi historia *(History of the two worlds), 1617–21, shows the creation of light from dark emptiness.*

theories. Interrogating the status quo is encouraged, as challenging the prevailing model either strengthens or refutes it. No narrative is fixed; every scientific tenet could be overturned tomorrow and science as a framework would remain the same.

Today we can harness technology and mathematics to work out how the universe really started, how it reached where it is at the moment, and where it might be headed. We can try to write its true story.

Still stories

Even with science, we have to start with tentative narratives, with suggestions of what might have been, and look for evidence to support or refute those ideas. The processes of the universe, of building stars, galaxies and planets, are so slow that we can never hope to understand them by watching them through time. Instead cosmologists and astronomers observe the myriad different phenomena around us and endeavour to piece together narratives and explanations

that fit their observations. Then they test their ideas with mathematics and further observations to see how well they hold up. There have been many false starts and a host of unexpected and sometimes unwelcome twists.

The ultimate story

The story of the universe is the biggest story of all – it describes all there is, was and ever will be, and tells of our attempt to understand it. There are two stories: one the narrative of the universe itself, from its first moments to now; the other the narrative of our discovery of it. These run in roughly opposite directions because the earliest moments of the universe have been uncovered most recently.

Our current understanding of the universe is set out in the Lambda Cold Dark Matter (LCDM) model, the standard version of Big Bang theory. But this doesn't give us the complete picture. Much of the story is still to be discovered.

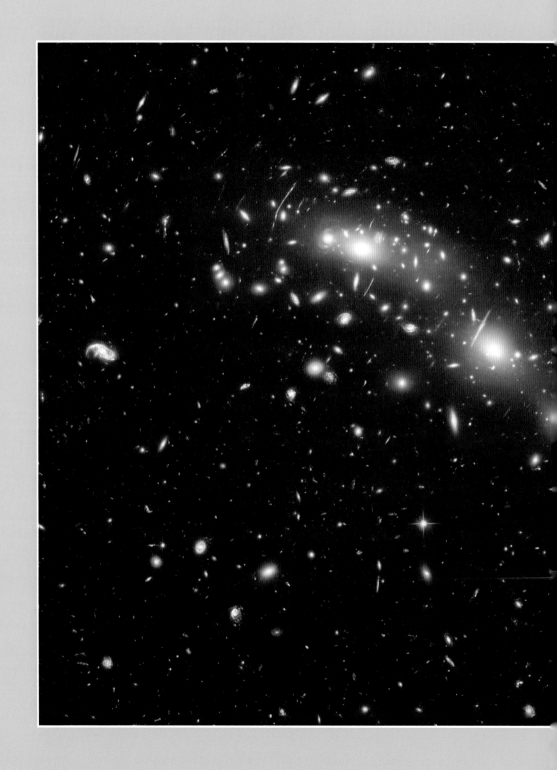

CHAPTER 1

THE 'DAY WITH NO YESTERDAY'

'The universe may be the ultimate free lunch.'

Alan Guth, 1992

Modern cosmology puts the origins of the universe between 12.5–13.8 billion years ago, in the 'Big Bang'. Space-time appeared at this first moment, apparently generated from nothing – everything else followed. It's a challenging idea, less than one hundred years old, yet it now shapes our story of the universe.

The inconceivable vastness of space is hinted at by images captured by the Hubble Space Telescope that show myriad galaxies the size of our Milky Way, each just a spot of light.

'Nothing will come of nothing'

The paradox of existence, why there is 'something' rather than 'nothing', began to be addressed rationally in Greece in the 5th century BC. The Ancient Greeks are the first people we know to have engaged in scientific thinking, trying to find the causes and nature of things through observation and reasoning rather than relying on supernatural explanations. There are only two obvious, broad explanations for the existence of anything: either it came into being at some point, or it was always there. Ancient Greece had proponents of each opinion.

A 17th-century engraving of Parmenides of Elea.

500 BC, another philosopher, Heraclitus, put it succinctly: 'This world-order [*kosmos*], the same of all, no god nor man did create, but it ever was and is and will be.'

Eternal matter

The philosopher Parmenides built an argument for an eternal, unchanging universe. Only fragments of his writings survive, and they are the earliest we have on the subject. He based his case around the opposition between what-is and what-is-not. 'What-is' can't in any way partake of 'what-is-not' – it can't make that leap. This means it can't have come into being, as to do so it would previously have been 'what-is-not', which is impossible. Similarly it can't be corrupted and cease to exist, as that suggests turning into 'what-is-not'. This leads to the conclusion that there can be no change, no movement and no void, and that everything is one unchanging thing. This seems counter to how we experience the world. Even so, the idea that things don't just spring from nowhere does seem intuitively appealing. Around

Steady as she goes

The notion that the universe is eternal and always pretty much the same was still the prevailing assumption at the start of the 20th century. It's now called a 'steady state' model of the universe, but until recently wasn't even thought of as a model – it was just how things were. The model was described by Isaac Newton in *Principia mathematica* in 1687, where he gave an account of an infinite, static, steady-state universe in which matter is uniformly distributed on the large scale. It was so thoroughly ingrained that when Albert Einstein derived his general relativity equations he soon after added a fudge, called the cosmological constant, to keep the universe steady. His assumption was that the universe doesn't change, and if his equations suggested it did, there was something wrong with them. He would later refer to this as the biggest blunder of his career.

Order from chaos

The opposite view has everything that exists being created from nothing, or from chaos. Imposing order on chaos is central to many creation myths. In the biblical book of Genesis, 'The earth was without form, and void' before God set about imposing some order on things. In order-from-chaos myths, there is some kind of disordered, chaotic primaeval matter from which everything is created through organization. But this is not quite the same as making something from nothing. God's creation of light just by speaking comes closer to that. Interestingly, the Catholic Church embraced Big Bang's confirmation of a moment of creation.

The Christian narrative of creation from nothing is depicted in mosaics on the inside of the dome of the Basilica of San Marco in Venice, Italy.

German scientist Otto von Guericke demonstrated the existence of a vacuum in 1654 with his 'Magdeburg hemispheres'. These were two metal half-domes which he fitted together and from which he then extracted the air with a pump. It took an immense force to separate them, as the pressure of the air around pushed them together.

'It would seem that present-day science, with one sweep back across the centuries, has succeeded in bearing witness to the august instant of the primordial Fiat Lux (Let there be Light), when along with matter, there burst forth from nothing a sea of light and radiation, and the elements split and churned and formed into millions of galaxies.'

Pope Pius XII, 1951

There is no nothing

The idea of something coming from nothing requires there to be some 'nothing'. The Ancient Greeks were divided over whether or not there could be a void (a space that contains no matter). The philosopher Aristotle argued in the 4th century BC that a void is impossible and nothing can be created except from some form of pre-existing matter, suggesting by implication that matter has always existed. Aristotle was sufficiently influential for this position to prevail for nearly 2,000 years. The nature of 'nothing' will turn out to be central to our current explanation of the universe.

If matter is continuous there is no empty space, but if matter is divided into tiny discrete portions (atoms in modern terminology) then empty space is essential, otherwise the particles are not separated. Once we accept the concept of empty space, there is still a need to define 'empty'. Experiments with vacuum pumps in the 17th century finally seemed to demonstrate that it is possible to have a space which contains no matter, even gas. But we now know that even outer space has a very low density of matter, even where it's only a few atoms per cubic metre. The best vacuum achieved by science is positively teeming with atoms, at up to 100,000 per cubic centimetre. Energy in the form of radiation can pass through empty space, and gravitational and magnetic fields can operate over an empty space. So just how empty is it?

Something for nothing?

Although the notion that nothing can be created out of nothing seems fundamental, it appears to be wrong. In high-speed particle accelerators, physicists crash subatomic particles together, creating great bursts of energy which manifest as particles. They are short-lived, winking in and out of existence in the nano-blink of an eye, but they exist. They are something created from nothing, or at least, matter created from energy. They are not some previous particles reconfigured; they are entirely new. It now appears that the origins of the universe lie in just such a springing into being from nothing.

It started with a bang

That which Parmenides would term 'what-is' sprang into existence 13.8 billion years ago from a singularity (see box below). All of 'what-is' now has emerged through

SINGLE AND MULTIPLE SINGULARITIES

A singularity in cosmology is an infinitely dense and infinitely small point. The Big Bang began with one singularity. There are other singularities at the hearts of black holes where matter has been squashed into an infinitely small volume.

populating space-time and from the change, rearrangement and spreading out of primeval 'stuff'. The story of the universe is the path from that singularity to the present day. An appendix to the story might be what could happen between now and the end of everything – if there is an end.

Big Bang theory replaced an earlier conception of the universe, and was built on human discoveries. It's hard to say where the story really starts: perhaps with Einstein

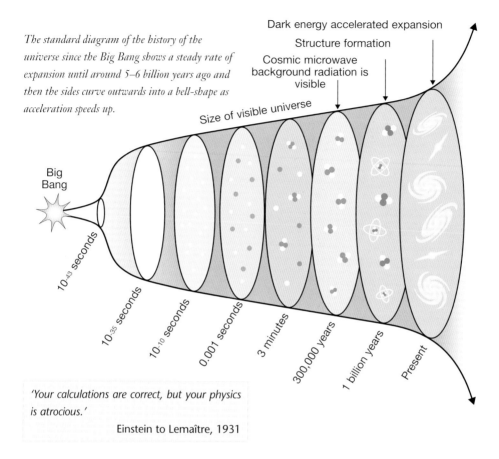

The standard diagram of the history of the universe since the Big Bang shows a steady rate of expansion until around 5–6 billion years ago and then the sides curve outwards into a bell-shape as acceleration speeds up.

Dark energy accelerated expansion

Structure formation

Cosmic microwave background radiation is visible

Size of visible universe

Big Bang

10^{-43} seconds

10^{-35} seconds

10^{-10} seconds

0.001 seconds

3 minutes

300,000 years

1 billion years

Present

'Your calculations are correct, but your physics is atrocious.'

Einstein to Lemaître, 1931

and the theory of general relativity; or with the American astronomer Henrietta Leavitt and the method of measuring the distance to some rather special stars; or with Isaac Newton and the nature of light and gravity. We will meet all these people as we work through the story of the universe. But we'll start in Belgium.

'Primeval atom'

The model we now call Big Bang theory was first proposed by Belgian priest and amateur astronomer Georges Lemaître in 1931. Through studying the mathematical explanation of gravity in Albert Einstein's General Theory of Relativity, published in 1915, Lemaître came to the realization in 1927 that the universe is expanding. He produced a set of solutions to the equations which indicated an expanding universe. Einstein, who favoured a steady-state universe, was not happy with this conclusion.

'The Big Bang, which is today posited as the origin of the world, does not contradict the divine act of creation; rather, it requires it.'

Pope Francis, 2014

If the universe is expanding, it must be expanding from something – it must previously have been smaller, a great deal smaller. This was the conclusion Lemaître expounded in 1931, suggesting that the whole universe must once have been a single incredibly dense point (a singularity). He coined the term 'primeval atom' for the entity which he saw as 'exploding at the point of Creation' – a neat marriage of cosmology and religion for an astronomer-priest.

GEORGES LEMAÎTRE (1894–1966)

Born at Charleroi, Belgium, Georges Lemaître was educated at a Jesuit secondary school and studied civil engineering at the Catholic University of Leuven. His studies were interrupted by World War I, but afterwards he studied physics and mathematics while preparing for the priesthood. He gained his PhD in 1920 and was ordained in 1923. The same year he moved to Cambridge University in England to work with the great astronomer Arthur Eddington, who introduced him to cosmology. Lemaître spent the following year at Harvard College Observatory and MIT, returning to Belgium in 1925 where he taught and researched at the University of Leuven until his retirement in 1964.

In 1927, Lemaître found a set of solutions to Einstein's general relativity equations that described an expanding universe. He published his solutions the same year. His paper included the first statement of what is now known as the Hubble–Lemaître law: that the speed at which objects move away from us in the universe is proportional to their distance from us. He also gave the first approximate value for Hubble's Constant, the rate of expansion of the universe. His work attracted little attention, largely because it was published in French.

Then, in 1931, at a conference in London about spirituality and the physical universe, Lemaître suggested that if the universe is expanding it must be expanding from something, and that if we go back far enough in time it must originally have been a small, compact point. Eddington called the idea 'repugnant' and Einstein initially thought it wrong, though he later concurred, and proposed Lemaître for the Belgian Francqui Prize for science in 1934. The 'primeval atom' gained more coverage than Lemaître's original paper, and soon he was famous. He won honours and awards and saw his theory acquire the name 'Big Bang'.

'As a scientist I simply do not believe that the universe began with a bang.'

Arthur Eddington, 1928

The beginning of the beginning

Lemaître looked to astronomy for evidence to support his theory. Two brilliant astronomers, Henrietta Leavitt and Edwin Hubble, had prepared the ground.

Bright and dim

Leavitt worked, initially as a volunteer, at the Harvard College Observatory from 1895 until her death in 1921. She studied variable stars and in particular Cepheid variable stars in the Magellanic Clouds, two dwarf galaxies visible in the southern hemisphere. Cepheids change their brightness at very regular intervals. In 1908, using some sophisticated mathematics and detailed observations, she realized that there is a direct correlation between the magnitude (brilliance) of a star and the length of time it is luminous before it dims: the brighter the star, the longer it remains luminous. From a complete cycle of dimming and brightening, Leavitt could calculate a star's magnitude. In 1912, she published a chart of 25 Cepheid periods and their apparent magnitude, from which their distance could be calculated.

Before Leavitt's work, astronomers could only calculate the distance to stars within 100 light years of Earth, which they did by using the method of parallax. The distance to the Cepheids of the Magellanic Clouds was up to 200,000 light years from Earth. Leavitt's method worked for distances of up to 10 million light years away. Called the 'yardstick to the universe', her discovery was an essential tool for Edwin Hubble, who laid the groundwork for Lemaître's findings.

PARALLAX

Parallax allows us to calculate the distance to an object by viewing it from two different positions. You can test this by holding a finger in front of your face and looking at it first with one eye closed and then with the other. The finger seems to jump from side to side. Parallax can be used to find the distance to astronomical objects using the Earth's position at opposite sides of its orbit (June and December) and measuring the angle between the lines of sight.

HENRIETTA SWAN LEAVITT (1868–1921)

Born in Cambridge, Massachusetts, Leavitt attended Oberlin College and the Society for the Collegiate Instruction of Women (later Radcliffe College) where she first discovered astronomy in 1892. Her studies were interrupted for several years by a serious illness which left her profoundly deaf. In 1895, she volunteered at Harvard College Observatory and seven years later was appointed to the permanent staff by director Charles Pickering, studying photos of stars to determine their magnitude.

The constraints of the day did not allow Leavitt, as a woman, to pursue her own theoretical work and design her own projects. Even so, she identified more than 2,400 variable stars – over half of those known at the time – and discovered the relationship between the variability and magnitude of Cepheid variable stars. She also developed the Harvard Standard for photographic measurements of the magnitude of stars. Leavitt worked at the Observatory until her death from cancer at the age of 53.

RS Puppis is one of the brightest Cepheid variable stars in the Milky Way. Its variable period is 41.5 days. RS Puppis is at the centre of this nebula, 6,000 light years away.

CEPHEID VARIABLE STARS

Cepheids are named after the star Delta Cephei, identified as variable by English amateur astronomer John Goodricke in 1784. The first Cepheid variable discovered was Eta Aquilae, found a few months previously by another English astronomer, Edward Pigott. Classical Cepheids are relatively recently formed stars which are four to 20 times more massive than Earth's Sun and up to 100,000 times more luminous. Their luminosity varies following a regular pattern over days and months. The radius of a Cepheid changes by millions of kilometres over the course of its variable cycle. This is caused, as suggested by Eddington in 1917, by changes in the temperature of the star which make it expand and contract. In 1953, Soviet astrophysicist Sergei Zhevakin identified a cycle by which helium ionizes and de-ionizes as the mechanism that was driving the process. Helium that is doubly ionized (has lost both its electrons) becomes opaque. As the star's atmosphere is heated from within, the heat can't escape through the opaque gas and as a consequence the atmosphere expands. The star cools as it grows, becoming de-ionized and returning to its transparent state.

Finding 'island universes'

We now know that the Magellanic Clouds are galaxies beyond the Milky Way. The 'nebulae' (fuzzy clouds of light) were first listed in 1771 by French astronomer Charles Messier (see box below). Their discovery had considerable implications for the size of the universe. On one side of the argument, Harlow Shapley, head of the Harvard College Observatory, believed that the Milky Way comprises the entire universe, and the spiral nebulae are relatively small features lying within its bounds. On the other side, Heber Curtis, director of the Allegheny Observatory in Pittsburgh, argued that the spiral nebulae lie outside our galaxy. He believed they are extremely large and very far distant, forming independent galaxies or 'island universes' as suggested by the philosopher Immanuel Kant in the 18th century.

On 26 April 1920, at the Smithsonian Museum of Natural History in Washington, D.C., both sides put their arguments in a 'great debate' involving eminent cosmologists of the day – but it resolved nothing. In 1924, American astronomer Edwin Hubble, using Leavitt's method, worked out that a Cepheid in the fuzzy patch of Andromeda is about eight times as far away from Earth as any star in the Milky Way. This stunning discovery was the first evidence that there could be something beyond our own galaxy. Hubble's conclusion that Andromeda is a galaxy instantly expanded the universe from a single galaxy to something potentially infinite in scope. How many more galaxies might there be?

Having discovered that the nebulae could be galaxies, Hubble set about classifying them according to their shape, patterns of brilliance and distance from Earth. By the end of the 1920s, he had found more than 20 additional galaxies and established different forms of galaxy – spiral, elliptical and irregular – that are still recognized today.

CLOUDS IN SPACE

Charles Messier (1730–1817) was not initially searching for nebulae, but for comets. The return of Halley's comet in 1758 sparked public and professional interest in these passing objects, and Messier decided to look for more, eventually finding 15 of them. In September 1758, he noticed a cloudy object in the night sky in the constellation of Taurus. As it didn't move, it clearly wasn't a comet. He decided to keep a list of all the stable nebulous objects he found to avoid mistaking them for comets. The object he had seen was the Crab nebula, which became the first object in his catalogue of nebulous objects, M1. It is now identified as the supernova remnant of a star that exploded in 1054, so is also known as SN1054.

The first edition of Messier's catalogue, published in 1771, listed 45 nebulous objects (Messier had discovered 17 of them). He and his colleagues continued to list objects, with 103 included in 1781 in the final edition of the catalogue to be published during his life. Further objects have been added since and the count now stands at 110, with the most recent, a dwarf elliptical galaxy in the Andromeda constellation, added in 1967.

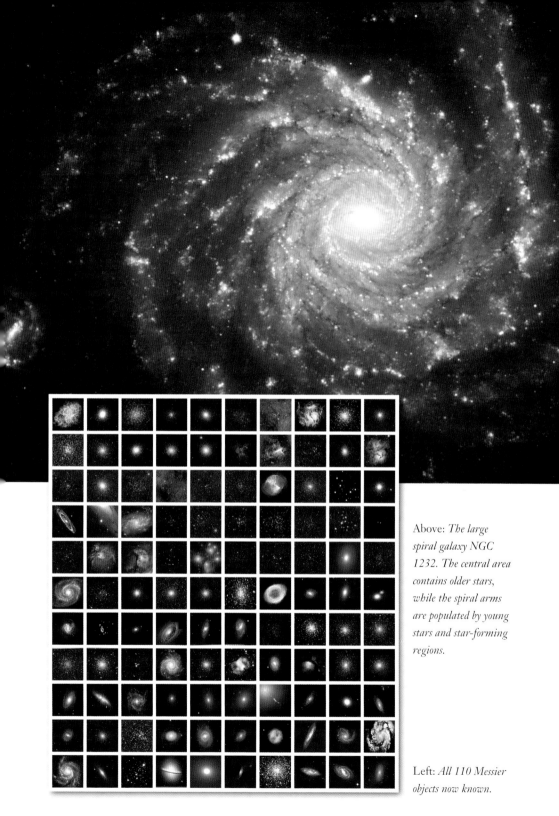

Above: *The large spiral galaxy NGC 1232. The central area contains older stars, while the spiral arms are populated by young stars and star-forming regions.*

Left: *All 110 Messier objects now known.*

Expanding evidence

The existence of galaxies beyond the Milky Way was a key piece of evidence for Lemaître, but he also used the work of another American astronomer who is often unfairly neglected.

In 1914, Vesto Slipher (1875–1969) presented the American Astronomical Society with his results from measuring the redshifts and blueshifts of nebulae (see box opposite). These indicate the movement of objects relative to an observer. Of 15 nebulae, 11 had redshifted light, meaning that the objects are moving away from us. By 1917, Slipher had identified 21 redshifted and four blueshifted nebulae. He noted: 'For us to have such motion and

the stars not show it means that our whole stellar system moves and carries us with it. It has for a long time been suggested that the spiral nebulae are stellar systems seen at great distances. . . . This theory, it seems to me, gains favour in the present observations.' By 1922, Slipher had data for 41 nebulae observable from the northern hemisphere. Although Eddington remarked it was 'very striking' that most of the nebulae seemed to be receding, he felt no conclusion could be drawn without data from the southern hemisphere. Gustaf Strömberg, a Swedish astronomer working at Mount Wilson Observatory in California, published Slipher's list of redshifts in 1925, so making them available to Lemaître.

Messier 74, or the Phantom galaxy, is a classic spiral galaxy 32 million light years away. It was discovered in 1780.

REDSHIFT, BLUESHIFT

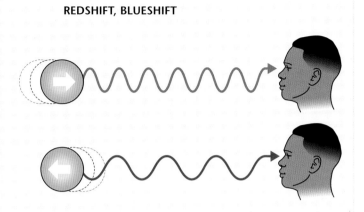

Redshift and blueshift affect light in the same way as the Doppler effect leads to the rise and fall of a siren as a vehicle approaches and then passes by. The effect was first described and explained in 1845 by Austrian mathematician Christian Doppler. If a sound source is moving towards you,

Light from a star moving towards Earth is blueshifted, looking bluer than the light that was emitted. Light from a star moving away from Earth is redshifted and looks redder.

the crest of each sound wave is emitted closer to you than the last. The effect is to bunch up the waves, reducing the wavelength and increasing the frequency, giving the sound a higher pitch. If a sound source is moving away from you, the opposite effect spreads out the wave crests. This increases the wavelength, decreasing the frequency and producing sound of a lower pitch. Doppler demonstrated his theory in a charming experiment that involved musicians playing instruments on a moving train while other musicians outside the train wrote down the notes they could hear. With considerable prescience, he proposed that the experiment would also work with light and would affect the apparent colour of distant stars.

Starting at the middle of the spectrum of visible light, increasing the wavelength moves light towards the red end of the spectrum, while decreasing the wavelength moves it towards the blue end of the spectrum. As a distant object moves away from the observer, the wavelength of light coming from it is stretched, so shifts it towards the red end of the spectrum (with longer wavelength), and the object looks redder than it is. An object moving towards the observer produces a blueshift: the wavelength of the light shortens and the object looks bluer than it is. From the perceived redshift or blueshift, an astronomer can tell whether a star is moving towards Earth or away from it (or is stationary with respect to Earth, producing no change).

'It is almost to be accepted with certainty that this will in the not too distant future offer astronomers a welcome means to determine the movements and distances of such stars which, because of their unmeasurable distances from us and the consequent smallness of the parallactic angles, until this moment hardly presented the hope of such measurements and determinations.'

Christian Doppler, 1842

Messier 32, an elliptical dwarf galaxy, is seen here as a white light just to the left of the Andromeda galaxy. It was discovered in 1749 and is 2.65 million light years away from Earth.

How far, how fast?

Lemaître had deduced from his work with Einstein's equations that the universe is not static but expanding. He then used Slipher's velocities of moving galaxies and the distances to those galaxies published by Hubble to calculate the rate at which the universe is expanding, coming up with a figure of 625 km per second per megaparsec. A megaparsec is one million parsecs, and a parsec is 3.26 light-years (30 trillion km or 19 trillion miles). The strange units for the rate come from plotting the rate of redshift of a galaxy in kilometres per second against its distance from Earth in megaparsecs.

The rate at which the universe is expanding is now known as Hubble's Constant, and the law defining it was at first called Hubble's Law (renamed the Hubble–Lemaître law in 2018). In 1929, Hubble and his assistant Milton Humason used better distances that they had measured, along with Slipher's redshift data, to state the law and their calculation of the constant, giving a value of about 500 km per second per megaparsec.

Most cosmologists preferred a different explanation for the expanding universe. They didn't deny it was expanding, but refused to accept that this meant it had once winked into existence as something very tiny. The steady-state or 'continual creation' theory was first set out by James Jeans around 1920 and refined in 1948 by Fred Hoyle, Hermann Bondi and Thomas Gold. It suggests that new material is constantly created as the universe expands so it always remains the same density and always looks the same. The new material forms the building blocks of stars and galaxies, and objects of different ages are distributed evenly throughout the universe. Any observer will always see a universe identical on the large scale, from any position and at any time. It is, in this model, eternal, with no beginning or end in time.

Flagging light

Another explanation was offered by Swiss astronomer Fritz Zwicky, who proposed the 'tired light' hypothesis. This suggests that the light is redshifted because it has lost energy travelling such a long distance, rather than because the galaxy is moving away from us. Both expanding-universe and tired-light theories would explain distant galaxies and stars looking dimmer than they really are.

Additional complications such as time dilation and other aspects of relativity make distant galaxies even dimmer in the expanding-universe model, but not in the tired-light model. We know that young stars and galaxies are brighter than older ones. If the predictions of both theories are combined with the observed brightness of distant galaxies, the expanding-universe model wins hands down. Young stars and galaxies would need to be dimmer, growing brighter as they age, for the tired-light theory to be correct.

The Bang gets bigger

Despite an initially underwhelming response, Lemaître's proposal began to gain attention, but it was not a fully developed cosmological model so many took it less than seriously. That changed in 1948 with the publication of a landmark paper by George Gamow, Ralph Alpher and Hans Bethe. (Bethe had been asked to take part so that the paper's authors could be listed as Alpher, Bethe and Gamow, an intellectual joke about the first three letters of the Greek alphabet – alpha, beta and gamma.)

Gamow was a Soviet chemist who had defected to the United States in 1934 and was trying to account for the relative abundance of different chemicals in the universe. He began to wonder whether conditions in the early universe could have favoured the creation of helium and perhaps other elements. Working with a young PhD student, Ralph Alpher, he examined the idea of the universe starting as a dense, intense point and expanding from there.

Irregular galaxies have no defined shape or structure. They are generally smaller than spiral or elliptical galaxies. Some might once have had a different structure but have been deformed by an external gravitational force. This image is of the dwarf irregular galaxy NGC 6822.

23

FIRST PARTICLES

Gamow and Alpher concluded that the early universe contained:

- protons – positively charged particles with slightly less mass than a neutron. A proton's positive charge exactly balances the negative charge of an electron.

- neutrons – uncharged particles found in the nuclei of atoms.

- electrons – negatively charged particles that have very low mass.

- neutrinos – uncharged particles that have very tiny, possibly zero, mass; one of the most abundant types of particle in the universe.

Gamow and Alpher began with a dense cloud of neutrons (see box above) as their original universe, which they called 'ylem' after an obsolete Middle English word for primordial substance. In their account, hot compressed neutrons would decay into a mixture of protons, electrons and neutrinos as the hot universe expanded. Then the protons would capture some of the neutrons to form deuterium nuclei (heavy hydrogen, with a proton and a neutron). Gamow and Alpher proposed that more and more neutrons would be captured, making heavier and heavier atomic nuclei to create the different elements, until eventually the expanding universe cooled to such an extent that no more reactions could take place. They published a paper in *Physical Review* with the title: 'The Origin of Chemical Elements.'

Although they were wrong about the addition of ever more neutrons, Gamow and Alpher were correct about progressing from protons (hydrogen nuclei) to deuterium and helium, so had successfully accounted for about 99 per cent of the mass of the universe. Just as importantly, they had given the Big Bang (though not yet called by that name) the status of a proper cosmological model. The Alpher–Bethe–Gamow paper brought Lemaître's model into the mainstream of cosmological debate, but it was still far from universally popular.

More bang for more bucks

It seemed that cosmology had reached an impasse. In the 1950s, however, evidence started to build in favour of the Big Bang. A new tool was brought to the debate – the radio telescope – as important for modern cosmology as the optical telescope had been for observational astronomy in the early 17th century.

Signals from space

The radio telescope came about following a discovery made by American radio engineer Karl Jansky. Like many great discoveries, it was accidental. Jansky was working for Bell Laboratories, investigating the sources of interference that might disturb short-wavelength radio transmissions across the

Atlantic. In 1931 he built a radio antenna on a turntable and recorded all the sources of static he could track over several months. He separated nearby and distant thunderstorms, but was left with a constant background hiss which he could not trace. After a while, he found that the brightest source of interference

George Gamow was one of the first scientists to use the Big Bang model.

repeated its signal every 23 hours and 56 minutes. This is the length of the sidereal day – the time it takes for the Earth to rotate relative to the stars. The signal appeared to be coming from the direction of the centre of the Milky Way. From this evidence, Jansky concluded that objects in space must emit radio waves.

He wanted to follow up his discovery and asked for permission to build a 30-metre (100-foot) radio antenna, but Bell wasn't interested in doing so because it would have no impact on the commercial uses of radio. Jansky's involvement with radio astronomy came to an abrupt end.

WHAT'S IN A NAME?

English astronomer Fred Hoyle was a proponent of the steady-state theory of the universe. In 1949 he criticized as 'irrational' and unscientific 'the hypothesis that all matter of the universe was created in one big bang at a particular time in the remote past'. (The claim that the Big Bang was unscientific was based on the argument that it referenced a moment of creation which looked suspiciously religious.)

It took several years for the term 'Big Bang' to become the standard label for the contentious model. The first research paper to use the term was published in 1966 by English physicists Stephen Hawking and Roger Tayler, and it came to be generally used from the late 1970s. Another name, which sadly didn't catch on, was bestowed by another detractor. Yale philosopher Norwood Russell Hanson referred to the 'Disneyoid picture' of a universe exploding into existence.

Karl Janksy's original rotating radio antenna – nicknamed the Merry-go-round – with which he detected radio signals from the heart of the Milky Way.

The Great Depression wasn't a good time to try to persuade anyone to fund a new project of no clear commercial value. No further progress was made until Grote Reber, a ham radio enthusiast, built the first radio telescope in his suburban backyard in Chicago. Before he found radio waves from space, he had to build three different parabolic dish reflectors, dropping the frequency he was receiving first from 3300 MHz to 900 MHz and finally to 160 MHz. In 1938 he picked up his first signal from the Milky Way.

Reber drew contour maps of the intensity of radio emissions he could detect across the sky. The brightest spot was in the centre of the Milky Way, but he also identified Cygnus and Cassiopeia. From 1938–43 he regularly publicized his findings in astronomy and engineering circles. When radio astronomy took off after World War II, the first radio astronomy department was set up at the University of Ohio.

Hubble's work with distant galaxies was all done with optical telescopes. If an object was so far away that its light was too dim to detect, he didn't know it existed. The most distant object he listed in his article of 1929 was, by his calculation, two megaparsecs away. This was about 6.5 million light years from the solar system – well outside the Milky Way, but a tiny distance in astronomical terms. The advent of the radio telescope produced some astounding evidence for the expansion of the universe, introducing objects at previously unimagined distances.

Rogue galaxies

As radio astronomers observed galaxies, they found some unusual and inexplicable objects –very bright radio sources that emitted on several frequencies. The objects were given the name 'quasi-stellar objects', which meant 'things like stars but probably not stars'. It was soon shortened to 'quasar'. By 1960, hundreds of quasars had been found, but none had been seen.

Grote Reber with his parabolic radio telescope. He built it in Illinois, but it is now sited in West Virginia.

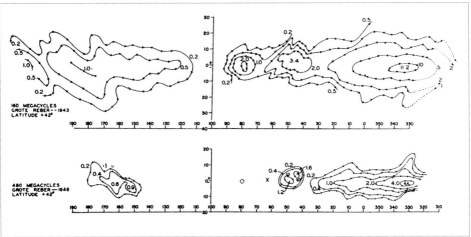

Reber's contour maps of radio signals show the highest concentration of radiation at the centre of the Milky Way.

A visible light source was first matched to a quasar in 1963 but far from solving the mystery, it deepened it. The faint, blue light source at the location of quasar 3C 48 had an unrecognized emission spectrum, meaning astronomers could not work out its composition.

Then, in 1962, Dutch astronomer Maarten Schmidt found a visible object corresponding to another quasar, 3C 273, and recorded its emission spectrum (see page 28). Again it had broad bands which didn't match known elements; Schmidt proposed they were hydrogen, massively redshifted. This means that the pattern of lines (the spacing between them) was the same, but the whole block was moved towards the red end of the spectrum. The redshift of nearly 16 per cent was far more than had ever been seen before; if caused by the star's movement it would mean it was moving away at an unimaginable rate of 47,000 km per second (29,000 miles per second). Nothing could explain this or account for the intense radio emissions of the object. Further examination of the spectrum of 3C 273 showed it to be hydrogen and magnesium redshifted by a massive 37 per cent.

Although the redshift was beyond contention, few astronomers were prepared to accept its implications for the velocity of the star. There seemed to be two possible explanations. The first posited that the star could be a very distant, very powerful object moving away very rapidly. The second suggested it could be a less powerful object,

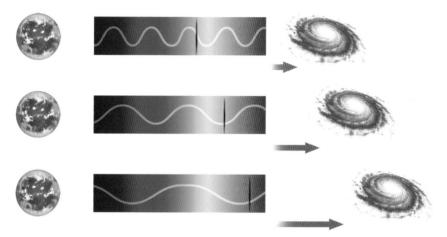

An undistorted emission spectrum (top) and the same spectrum redshifted (two illustrations beneath). The pattern is the same, but the wavelengths of the light have shifted to the right.

LIGHT FROM THE STARS

All chemical elements emit light when heated, and each one emits light of a specific wavelength. The pattern of bands of light of different wavelengths emitted by a star or other luminous object is called its emission spectrum. Astronomers use emission spectra to identify the chemical components of stars and atmospheres.

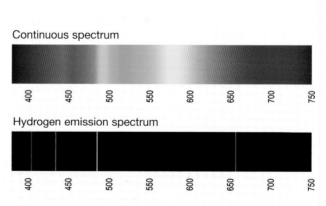

The emission spectrum of hydrogen (bottom) compared with the continuous spectrum of visible light (above).

QUASARS UNRAVELLED

Quasars lie at the heart of active galaxies where they are powered by matter surrounding a massive black hole. As material near the black hole is drawn towards it, gravitational stress and friction produce the immense energy of the quasar. Quasars are among the most powerful energy-producing objects in the universe. They emit radiation at all wavelengths, but their visible light is faint because they are so distant from us. If quasar 3C 273 were just 33 light years away, it would appear as bright as the Sun does now (which is only 8 light minutes away); it shines four trillion times more brightly, emitting around 100 times as much light as the entire Milky Way.

much closer to Earth, a star perhaps only 10 km (6 miles) wide situated near or inside the Milky Way, and the emissions of this object were undergoing redshift for some reason other than velocity.

Most astronomers preferred the second explanation, and deduced that the redshift was either the result of gravity (the mass of the object distorting its own emissions) or some so far unknown process. Schmidt, however, favoured the first explanation. Although the theory of the very distant fast-moving object was widely rejected, it turned out to be correct. But it would take further advances in astronomy before the true situation could be revealed and the remoteness of quasars confirmed. Now more than 200,000 quasars are known, with the most distant around 29 billion light years away. That's a huge increase on Hubble's galaxies, just two million light years hence.

An echo from the past

Quasars were the first evidence that some objects are moving from us at an incredibly fast rate and are an immense distance away, in keeping with the predictions of Big Bang theory. As the estimated size of the universe increased, its genesis from an infinitely small point looked more and more improbable to opponents of the Big Bang model. But before the significance of quasars was understood, another accidental radio discovery provided the next piece of evidence in favour of the Big Bang. Again, Bell Laboratories played a part.

In 1962, two radio engineers at Bell, Arno Penzias and Robert Wilson, were trying to work out the source of interference in a radio signal. They managed to eliminate all extraneous signals but found there was still a faint background noise which covered the entire sky, day and night, without change. At this point they heard about work suggesting that an echo of the Big Bang might still be detectable as background radiation in space. Penzias and Wilson realized that their mysterious interference was, in fact, billions of years old: it was the Cosmic Microwave Background (CMB) electromagnetic radiation left over from the beginnings of the universe.

CMB comes from a little later in the story of the universe than the first moment. We shall meet it again in Chapter 3. But at this point in the 1960s it was the first confirmation that the Big Bang was more than just a neat idea. Now scientists had the tricky task of unpicking exactly what it meant.

CHAPTER 2

THE FIRST MICROMOMENTS

'We have a viable theory of the universe back to about 10^{-30} seconds. At that time, the currently observable universe was smaller than the smallest dot on your TV screen, and less time had passed than it takes for light to cross that dot.'

George F. Smoot,
Nobel Prize in Physics, 2006

It is in the very first moments of the universe that we must seek the clues to how it has come about and what it is like. The fundamental particles of matter that would eventually build into everything we know came into existence during the first second of time.

An Ancient Egyptian depiction of the birth of the universe, showing the Sun rising from the Mound of Creation at the beginning of time. The Sun appears as an orange disk at three stages of its procession across the heavens. At either side are the goddesses of the north and south, pouring out primeval waters. On the land, eight Ogdoad deities hoe the soil.

Starting from zero

Scientists divide the history of the universe into epochs, characterized by different types of activity. We tend to think of epochs as long periods of time, but the first epochs in the story of the universe lasted for unimaginably tiny fractions of a second. The first epoch, called the Planck epoch (or era) ran from the instant of the Big Bang to 10^{-44} second. It's an inconceivably brief instant of time: 1/100,000,000,0 00,000,000,000,000,000,000,000,000, 000,000,000 of a second. The start of this epoch was the moment of the Big Bang, when the universe was infinitely dense and infinitely small – a singularity. The laws of physics don't work in such a situation, so there's nothing much we can say about it.

The next epoch was a little longer, but not much – the universe managed to cram six epochs into the first second of its existence. The seventh epoch lasted a full three minutes. By the end of that time, the four fundamental forces had separated themselves out and the first atomic nuclei had appeared. Working out what happened in this brief moment in time took physicists many years.

Something from nothing

Modern physics considers that quantum fluctuations caused the universe to pop into existence. It didn't appear in space because there was no space. Space was within the universe and defined by it.

The zero-energy universe theory proposed by Edward Tryon in 1973 uses a neat bit of thermodynamic balancing, which allows the universe to exist. As gravitational energy is negative, and the energy bound up in mass (matter) is positive, they cancel each other out. The universe had (and has) zero net energy. It was therefore possible for it to come into existence without violating any rules of energy conservation. It can blink out of existence at some point in the future or continue to exist forever.

Starting the clock

As space-time came into existence at the Big Bang, we start counting time from that point, when time=0 (or T_0). We are not able to ask what came before the Big Bang because 'before' has no meaning. This doesn't necessarily imply there was nothing, it simply means that the Big Bang reset everything. There may have been previous versions of the universe, or of many universes, which were recycled in the Big Bang. As no physical laws or states would have survived this moment, however, we can never know anything about them.

'Since events before the Big Bang have no observational consequences, one may as well cut them out of the theory, and say that time began at the Big Bang.'

Stephen Hawking, 2014

Dramatic forces are still at work in the universe, as this photograph of the colliding Antennae galaxies shows.

The universe gets going: the Planck epoch

It's thought that until around 5.4×10^{-44} seconds, the laws of physics did not apply to the tiny, nascent universe. The best physics can offer is that the universe sprang into being as the result of quantum fluctuations in the vacuum, although even 'vacuum' is hard to apprehend if there is no space-time. It's thought that quantum gravity predominated during the Planck epoch, but as we don't have any coherent theory of quantum gravity that really amounts to giving 'we don't know' a fancy-sounding name.

We'll have to let that first 10^{-44} second remain a mystery for the time being.

What we do have from that first moment of the universe are some units of measurement which are defined by it.

The kilogram was the last SI unit to have a physical standard – a cylinder of platinum-iridium. It was replaced in 2019 with a definition that ties it to the Planck constant and the speed of light.

Max Planck is considered one of the greatest physicists who ever lived. His work revolutionized our understanding of particles and energy.

The point at which space-time came into existence is also the point at which we can begin to measure it.

Natural units and the beginning of space-time

When we measure things – height, temperature, time, for instance – we use units. Early measurements of length were based on human body parts, such as the distance from hand to elbow or the length of a foot. To be useful, units have to be standardized (my foot might be smaller than yours, so we agree on a standard – the length of the emperor's foot, for example). Units based on a standard are only useful when it is known and available. When physicists want to measure fundamental things, they try to use 'natural units'. These are not based on anything that requires a standard, but are universal. The speed of light, given as c, is a natural unit. If we give

it in km/s, it's the same speed, but no longer expressed in a natural unit. If we ask an alien to send something at 300 km/s it will be meaningless to them. Asking them to send it at the speed of light will be unambiguous. They can think of it as furlongs per nanoday, or whatever their units are, but it will still be the speed of light. There are five natural units that physicists use when talking about the early history of the universe, and the speed of light is one of them.

Planck units are named in honour of the German physicist Max Planck, who set out his ideas about natural units in 1899. The first system was devised by Irish physicist George Johnstone Stoney in 1874 and was named the Stoney scale after him. Stoney realized that electrical charge is quantized – that is, it comes in tiny indivisible packets of a fixed size. He found he could derive natural units for length, mass and time by standardizing

> 'These necessarily retain their meaning for all times and for all civilizations, even extraterrestrial and non-human ones, and can therefore be designated as "natural units".'
>
> Max Planck, 1899

at 1 the values of the speed of light (c), the gravitational constant (G) and the charge on an electron (e). He aimed to simplify things that are otherwise quite complicated. An expression that gives the speed of light as 299,792,458 m/s (approximately 186,000 mi/s) is obviously simpler if the speed of light is simply written as '1'. Planck didn't include any electromagnetic units in his system, but derived natural units for length, time, mass and temperature. He was, of course, working long before anyone had any concept of the first nanomoments of the universe.

Planck units and time=0

Several Planck units are defined by the Planck epoch, ending at 10^{-44} s. The Planck units are set to 1 at this point.

• Planck length is the diameter of the universe at the end of the Planck epoch, which translates to 1.62×10^{-35} m.

The Irish physicist George Johnstone Stoney introduced the term 'electron' for the 'fundamental unit of electricity'.

WHEN DID T=0?

If the universe is eternal and unending, it doesn't have an age. But a Big Bang theory begs the question, when? Meaningful calculation could only begin in the 20th century, using two methods: looking for the oldest stars and working out from the rate of the universe's expansion when it must have started. The best figures from measuring cosmic microwave background radiation were 13.772 ± 0.059 billion years, calculated in 2012, and 13.813 ±0.038 billion years, calculated in 2013. The lower end of the 2103 figure falls within the 2012 range, so all looked good. Estimates from the age of stars were a bit different until 2019. Then new measurements from data collected by the Hubble Space Telescope suggested the universe could be a billion years younger. Astrophysicists are still trying to work out which figure – if either – is correct and whether we need to adjust our model of the evolution of the universe.

HOT AND COLD IN KELVIN

Physicists measure temperature using kelvin (K), rather than degrees Celsius. The unit is exactly the same as 1 degree Celsius but the baseline is absolute zero, the coldest possible temperature, which is $-273.15°C$ ($-459.67°F$). The boiling point of water, then, is 373.15 K. (There is no degree symbol used with temperatures in kelvin.) Absolute zero is the coldest temperature theoretically possible because it is the point at which atoms stop moving. They can't move less than not at all, so nothing can be colder.

- Planck time, the smallest meaningful unit of time, is the length of time it takes for a photon to travel the Planck distance (to travel across the nascent universe at the speed of light). As light travels at approximately 300,000 km/s, it doesn't take long to travel that tiny distance. The Planck time is 5.39×10^{-44} s.

These measurements are very small, but the Planck temperature is very large:

- Planck temperature represents the temperature of the universe at the end of the Planck epoch, which translates to 1.41×10^{32} kelvin (K).

The speed of light, generally considered to have been the same through all time, is now and was at the end of the Planck epoch 299,792,458 m/s.

The end of an epoch

At the end of the Planck epoch, everything was set to 1: Planck time, Planck length, Planck temperature and the speed of light. At the start, the Planck length had been 0 and the temperature infinite. In between, cosmologists suggest that the four fundamental forces which would later structure the universe were combined in a single force. Physics becomes capable of modelling something of the universe only at the end of the Planck epoch. At this point, when the temperature had dropped to 10^{32} K, the first of the forces, gravity, 'froze' out of the unified force. The density of the universe was a staggering 10^{94} grams per cubic centimetre.

Things fall apart

The Grand Unification epoch followed the Planck epoch. It ran from 10^{-43} s to 10^{-36} s.

INCONSTANT CONSTANTS

Several physicists have suggested that the 'constants' upon which cosmological and other calculations rely might not actually be constant. What if the speed of light was faster or slower in the past. Would we know? How could we tell? And would it matter? Theories suggesting the inconstancy of accepted constants crop up now and then, but most scientists view them with a degree of scepticism. George Gamow (see page 23) wrote a series of popular science books concerning the adventures of Mr Tompkins in which some of the universal constants are changed. In the first story, Mr Tompkins enters a dream world where the speed of light is 4.5 m/s.

FEEL THE FORCES

There are four basic natural forces: gravity, the strong nuclear force, the weak nuclear force and electromagnetic force.

- Gravity acts between objects of mass, drawing them together. It keeps the planets in orbit around the Sun. Gravity has always been evident, and was first mathematically described by Isaac Newton in *Principia mathematica* published in 1687.

- The strong nuclear force is the strongest of the four natural forces. It holds subatomic particles together, fusing quarks to form larger particles (see page 42). The behaviour of the strong force was described in the early 1970s, before the existence of quarks and gluons (elementary particles that hold quarks together) had been confirmed.

- The weak nuclear force is also stronger than gravity but operates over only very short distances between subatomic particles. It's implicated in radioactive decay, powering stars and creating elements (see page 38). It was first proposed by the Italian-American physicist Enrico Fermi in 1933 and demonstrated experimentally in the 1970s and 1980s.

- Electromagnetic force operates between electrically charged particles. It holds electrons in orbit within atoms and forms bonds between atoms. Electromagnetism was first properly described by James Clerk Maxwell in 1873.

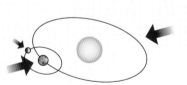

Gravitational force binds
the solar system

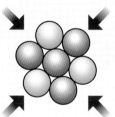

Strong force binds
the nucleus

Weak force is involved
in radioactive decay

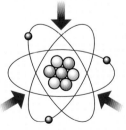

Electromagnetic force
binds atoms

Cosmologists believe that at this point the remaining three forces, the strong, weak and electromagnetic, were still combined. They call this combination of forces the electronuclear force.

At the end of the Grand Unification epoch, the strong nuclear force broke free of the other two, leaving just the electroweak (the electromagnetic and weak forces) as a united force. In 1968, Sheldon Glashow, Abdus Salam and Steven Weinberg managed to create an electroweak force by compelling the weak and electromagnetic forces to come together under conditions of extreme energy. This proved that the electromagnetic and weak forces are different aspects of the same thing, which at very high temperatures can combine.

The temperature at the end of the Grand Unification epoch was 10^{27} K and the universe was still smaller than a single quark, the tiniest component of a subatomic particle. The separation of the

Pakistani physicist Abdus Salam shared a Nobel Prize in 1979 with Sheldon Glashow for their work on the electroweak force. He was the first person from a Muslim country to win a Nobel Prize in science.

strong nuclear interaction triggered the inflationary epoch, when things start to get exciting and the universe expanded massively in a tiny fraction of a second.

Hyper-inflation

Although the universe was expanding during the first two epochs, it wasn't going very quickly. If it had continued at the same rate, it still wouldn't be very big, relatively speaking. But decoupling the strong force unleashed a new kind of energy that led to brief, but exponential expansion. The diameter of the universe increased by a factor of 10^{26} in the infinitessimally brief period between 10^{-36} s and 10^{-33} s. It's an inconceivable level of expansion: like something the width of a DNA molecule (2 nanometres) expanding to about 200 trillion km (124 trillion miles), or more

BOSONS BEGIN

Bosons are fundamental particles that carry energy. They are distinct from fermions, which are particles that make up matter. Gauge bosons, also called force particles, mediate forces, which means they produce the forces identified in physics. There are four types of boson: photons produce the electromagnetic force, so are responsible for light, microwaves and so on; gluons produce the strong force – they act like glue, holding quarks together in subatomic particles; and W and Z bosons produce the weak force that is involved in radioactive decay.

than 20 light years. Increasing the linear dimension by a factor of 10^{26} increased the volume by 10^{78}. The universe was so tiny to start with that it was still far from huge at the end of cosmic inflation. Some theorists put it at the size of a grain of sand at the end of the Inflationary epoch, while others say it was the size of a grapefruit or a basketball, or even a few metres across. These are not very different at this kind of scale.

Proposing growth

The Inflationary epoch was first proposed by American physicist and cosmologist Alan Guth (b.1947) in 1980. He was looking for solutions to the issue of 'flatness' – the apparent shape of the universe (see page 199). Guth modelled a universe that underwent a very brief but rapid period of supercooling, which produced a near-exponential expansion he called 'cosmic inflation'. His model relied on the notion that gravity can become a repelling force, known as a false vacuum, at extremely high densities. The energy of the false vacuum pushes the parts of the universe apart, producing inflation.

American theoretical physicist Alan Guth proposed inflationary theory as a young research scientist.

ALL OR PART?

The cosmic inflation theory, and pretty much everything else in cosmology, applies to the observable universe. There might be more universe beyond what is observable, but we have no knowledge of it and no way of knowing its true size. It is relatively unlikely that we can see all of it; to do so we would have to be right in the middle of the universe (as we can observe equally far in all directions).

The observable universe is a sphere 93 billion light years across. Even though the universe is only 12.5–13.8 billion years old, we can observe objects 46.5 billion light years away, at the edge of the observable universe. This is because light from objects 46.5 billion light years away began its journey towards us when the universe was much smaller, so it has still had time to reach us.

This theory solved several problems, including those of flatness and homogeneity. The homogeneity of the observable universe had troubled cosmologists. Although the universe is vast it seems to be pretty much the same everywhere in terms of the cosmic microwave background radiation (see page 58) and the distribution of matter (on a large scale). The parts of the universe are too far apart for this homogeneity to be explained without the theory of cosmic inflation. In Guth's model, the expansion was so rapid that the dense homogeneity of the tiny universe did not have time to be disrupted as it expanded, so the universe simply became equally homogenous but more spaced out.

Faster than light – without moving

The idea that the universe might have expanded faster than the speed of light during the Inflationary epoch seems at first absurd, because nothing (according to Einstein) can travel faster than the speed of light. But expansion doesn't actually entail anything travelling. Space simply increases and the objects in space that separate as a result are not really moving – they just become more distant. The result is that areas of space which were adjacent before inflation may be so far apart after inflation that it is impossible for information or energy to travel between them. They are still separating, and the speed of light is too low for a photon ever to reach the receding destination.

A new field – briefly

It's not clear exactly what powered inflation. One theory is that the dissociation of the strong force produced a temporary field mediated by an odd type of boson not seen since called an 'inflaton'. The inflaton is the name given to both the boson and the field. It was not part of Guth's original inflationary model but was added later to make it more coherent and to avoid some problems. The inflaton would have driven inflation for the brief time it endured, and then decayed. With its decay, it populated

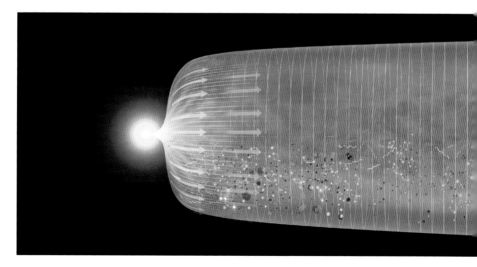

the universe with matter and radiation. In another possible model, inflation stopped in localized areas, including our observable universe, but has continued outside it and between universes (see page 203).

Stretching the emptiness

Remember that at the start of the Inflationary epoch there was still no matter in the universe, only quantum fields. We can think of the quantum fields as producing a sort of background hum, a level of vibration in the vacuum. There are tiny inequalities as the fields are not entirely evenly distributed. When inflation expanded the space in which the fields existed, it expanded even the tiny bumps and wiggles produced by the field, making them much larger. The fields were more intense in some places than in others. Because expansion was so rapid, regions that had previously been adjacent were so widely separated that they would never be able to communicate again. They were all effectively isolated. Overall, the structure was still homogenous, but on a smaller scale; the homogeneity was made up of very tiny local variations that evened out over the larger scale. This would later be massively important: slight bumps and inequalities would produce the grainy structure of the universe, determining the positioning of galaxy clusters and everything else.

The start of stuff

At the end of the Inflationary epoch, the huge potential energy of the inflation field was released, reheating the universe and populating it with the first particles of matter: a hot plasma of quarks, leptons and their corresponding anti-particles. This was the Quark epoch, and lasted until the end of the first millionth of a second, 10^{-6} s – a timescale that's almost graspable.

Cosmic inflation is represented in the sudden widening of the cone near the start of this timeline of the early universe. It continues to expand, but at a slower rate, after inflation.

From energy to matter

At the start of the Quark epoch, the temperature had cooled to about 10 quadrillion (10^{16}) degrees. This was still too hot for normal matter to form, but not for the precursors of matter. The energy of the collapsing inflation field instantly filled the universe with a hot, dense 'soup' or plasma of elementary particles. It was made up of different quarks, gluons, leptons and their opposites – the corresponding antimatter particles, anti-quarks and anti-leptons (see box below). Collisions between particles were so energetic that they could not stick together and form larger particles. Instead they broke the quarks, producing new particles as a result. These particles are labelled 'exotic' by physicists. They

INGREDIENTS FOR SOUP

The elementary particles in the soup were quarks, leptons and electrons.

- Quarks are the components of the subatomic particles, protons and neutrons. Each proton and neutron is made of three quarks. Quarks come in six 'flavours' (kinds), forming three pairs: up and down, strange and charm, and top and bottom. Each has a corresponding antimatter quark, called an antiquark. Quarks have an electrical charge, as we shall see later.

Three quarks held together by gluons form a nucleon.

- Gluons, as the name suggests, act like a kind of subatomic glue. They are bosons that mediate the strong nuclear force, holding quarks together when they form protons and neutrons.

- Leptons can be charged or neutral. They are not affected by the strong force (provided by gluons). There are six types of lepton. The three charged leptons are the electron, the tau and the muon (which are similar to the electron but have more mass). The three neutral leptons are neutrinos and have very small or zero mass.

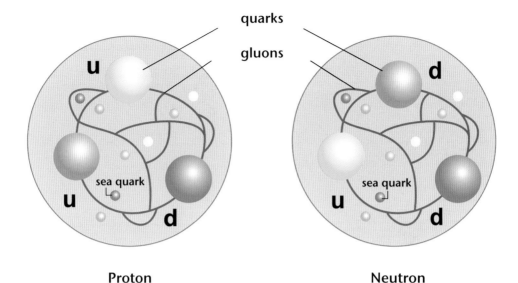

quarks

gluons

sea quark

u

u

d

Proton

d

d

sea quark

u

d

Neutron

Inside protons and neutrons, gluons hold the three valence quarks together. The gluons are constantly disintegrating into temporary 'sea quarks' and reforming. Sea quarks are virtual quark-antiquark pairs.

included W and Z bosons, possibly the Higgs boson, and gluons.

Sticking together

The main difference between quarks and leptons is that quarks are affected by all four of the fundamental forces, but leptons are unaffected by the strong force. This may not seem a big difference (it's only one force out of four) but it means that quarks can be irrevocably bound together into the stuff of ordinary matter, while leptons can escape.

Electrons are leptons and are a vital ingredient of atomic matter, but they can be prised out of an atom quite easily (when it is ionized, for example). Quarks can't be removed from the matter in which they are embedded. Once stuck together, they are pretty much there for all eternity.

Although quarks have existed since the first millionth of a second, no one knew about them until the 20th century. They were proposed independently by two physicists in 1964, the American-born Murray Gell-Mann and the Russian-American George Zweig. At the time it was generally thought that particles called hadrons, which include protons and neutrons, were fundamental – that is, they could not be broken down any further. Gell-Mann and Zweig proposed that hadrons are made up of smaller parts (quarks), that have electrical charge and spin. They proposed three types of quark: up, down and strange. Just months later, another was added: charm. The first evidence for the existence of quarks came in 1968 when work at the Stanford Linear Accelerator Center revealed that protons are not fundamental, but contain much smaller, point-like objects.

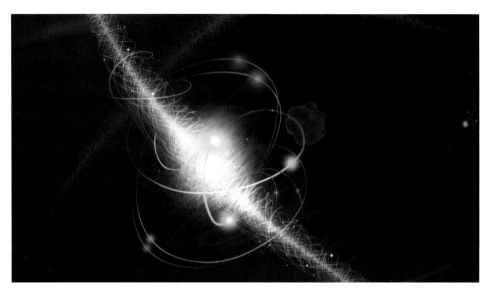

An artist's impression of an electron orbiting the nucleus of an atom. The nucleus is the distant grey body (far right).

Electrons – easier to spot

While there is little evidence of quarks and they had to be hunted for with some determination, electrons were spotted much sooner. They were the first subatomic particle to be discovered, found even before the existence of atoms was confirmed.

The idea that electrical charge might be divided into discrete electrical packets had first been suggested by George Johnstone Stoney in 1874 (see page 35). He proposed a 'single definite quantity of electricity', equal to the charge on a monovalent ion (that is, an ion with a charge of 1).

QUARK OR QUORK?

The word 'quark' is taken from a line in *Finnegan's Wake*, an experimental work of fiction by James Joyce. Murray Gell-Mann, proposer of the quark, explained how the term came to be adopted: 'In 1963, when I assigned the name "quark" to the fundamental constituents of the nucleon, I had the sound first, without the spelling, which could have been "kwork". Then, in one of my occasional perusals of *Finnegans Wake*, by James Joyce, I came across the word "quark" in the phrase "Three quarks for Muster Mark". Since "quark" (meaning, for one thing, the cry of the gull) was clearly intended to rhyme with "Mark", as well as "bark" and other such words, I had to find an excuse to pronounce it as "kwork". . . From time to time, phrases occur in the book that are partially determined by calls for drinks at the bar. I argued, therefore, that perhaps one of the multiple sources of the cry "Three quarks for Muster Mark" might be "Three quarts for Mister Mark", in which case the pronunciation "kwork" would not be totally unjustified. In any case, the number three fitted perfectly the way quarks occur in nature.'

He came up with the name 'electron' in 1894. Stoney thought the charges were irretrievably stuck to atoms and couldn't exist independently. He consequently saw no connection between his proposed quantized electrical charge and (a recent discovery) cathode rays.

In 1869, German physicist Johann Hittorf had found that passing electricity through a rarefied gas produced a green glow from the cathode (negative electrode). The glow increased as the quantity of gas present decreased. No one knew what the cathode rays were, and suggestions included waves, atoms or some kind of molecule. To investigate, Sir William Crookes made cathode ray tubes in the 1870s. It was while using one of these that English physicist J.J. Thomson identified the electron, the first subatomic particle.

Experimenting with a cathode ray tube and a magnet, Thomson found that the green beam was made up of negatively charged particles which he calculated had only about 1/1000th the weight of a hydrogen ion. The only way to explain it was that there was something smaller than an atom – some kind of subatomic particle. Previously atoms had been considered the smallest possible part of matter. The name 'atom' comes from the Greek *atomos*, or 'uncuttables', coined by the first philosophers to propose atoms in the 5th century BC. Thomson suggested that the atom is a cloud of positively charged material, balanced by the negative charge of electrons embedded in it. This became known as the 'plum pudding' model of the atom.

Thomson further showed that electrons were the same no matter which material was used as the cathode, and that the same particles could be produced by heated or illuminated materials and by radioactive matter. This was the first clue that all matter is made up of essentially identical components; the variations are produced by the number and configuration of electrons, protons and neutrons that make up different types of matter.

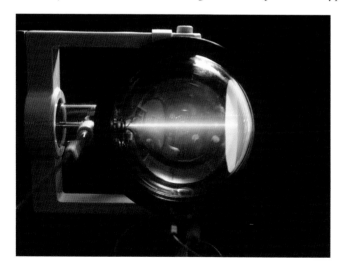

In a cathode ray tube, a focused beam of electrons travels through a vacuum and strikes a phosphorescent screen, making it glow.

45

MAKING QUARK SOUP

Physicists still don't know how the quark soup worked or behaved, but they managed to make some of their own. It was first achieved in 2000 at the Relativistic Heavy Ion Collider (RHIC) at Brookhaven National Laboratory in New York. Catastrophic collisions were caused using fast particle accelerators and heating the nuclei of heavy atoms such as gold or lead to temperatures higher than 2 trillion degrees Celsius (3.6 trillion degrees Fahrenheit), then blasting them towards each other as fast as possible. This shakes the quarks and gluons free, briefly recreating the primordial quark–gluon soup, before they fuse back together in a medley of random particles. The soup turns out to be a near-perfect liquid, flowing with virtually zero viscosity.

Lumps in the soup: from quarks to hadrons

At the end of the Quark epoch, at 10^{-6} s, conditions had cooled considerably, to about 10^{16} K. The universe was about the size of our solar system, around 12 billion km (7.5 billion miles) across. The effect of cooling meant the energy with which particles slammed into one another was reduced. When it fell below their binding energy, the particles clung together. The quarks were trapped forever, stuck together by gluons. After their brief but glorious epoch, they swapped a millionth of a second of freedom for billions of years tied up in matter. The electron remained free for 380,000 years until it, too, was incorporated into matter.

The quarks that stuck together formed hadrons; so the next epoch is dubbed the Hadron epoch. There are two classes of hadrons, known as baryons and mesons. Baryons are made of three quarks, while mesons generally have one quark and one anti-quark.

Most of the mass of ordinary matter in the universe consists of two types of baryons – these are protons and neutrons.

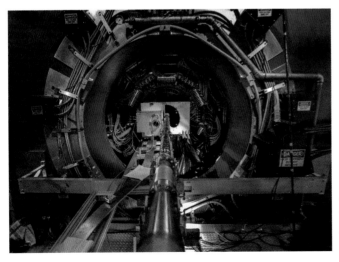

The Star detector at the Relativistic Heavy Ion Collider, where quarks have been briefly liberated from matter in high-energy collisions.

THE START OF STUFF

Together these form the nuclei of atoms. Taking the charge of the electron as -1, a proton has a charge of +1; a neutron has no charge. The first baryons formed were protons and antiprotons. A proton is made of two up-quarks and one down-quark. The up-quarks each bring a charge of +2/3, making +4/3, and the single down-quark brings -1/3, giving a result of +1. This is exactly opposite the charge of -1 on an electron. An antiproton has the same make-up but uses antiquarks, so -4/3 + 1/3 = -1.

A helium atom has two protons, two neutrons and two electrons. Each proton and neutron is made up of three quarks held together by gluons. The electrons are leptons and cannot be further broken down.

Clearing the decks

You would think if the protons were made by random collisions between quarks, there would be as many antiprotons created as protons (as much matter as antimatter). As an encounter between a matter particle and an antimatter particle results in disaster (they annihilate each other), this should lead to there being no matter in the universe. It means the experiment in creating a universe would have been brief, over in about a second. But luckily for us, there were approximately 1,000,000,001 protons for every 1,000,000,000 antiprotons. For every one billion mutual annihilations there was a proton remaining. This process – the formation of protons and antiprotons and the destruction of most of them – is called baryogenesis because it is the formation (genesis) of baryonic matter. It is the sort of matter things in the universe are made of, from stars to squids and sticky tape.

Into neutral

Protons have a positive charge of +1e. Occasionally a proton captures an electron, bringing in a negative charge, -1e, so giving the particle a net charge of zero. These enhanced protons are neutrons. By the end of the Hadron epoch there was about one neutron for every seven protons. This would dictate the balance of elements in the universe. Most atoms have a roughly equal number of protons and neutrons in their nucleus, but hydrogen alone has no neutrons. The hydrogen nucleus is a single proton. There were lots of spare protons during the Hadron epoch and the universe has a surplus of hydrogen – it is by far the most abundant element.

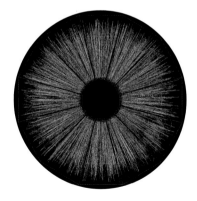

The end-view of a gold ion collision in the RHIC, momentarily freeing quarks and mimicking the quark–gluon plasma of the very early universe.

DOES NATURE PREFER MATTER TO ANTIMATTER?

It seems that the universe is slightly biased in favour of matter over antimatter – which is useful, as we wouldn't be here otherwise. Results from the Tevatron particle accelerator in the USA, analyzed in May 2010, showed that the decay of B mesons produced about 1 per cent more muons than anti-muons. (B mesons are made of an up, down, charm or strange quark combined with a bottom antiquark.)

Protons and neutrons were not the only type of hadrons to be created in the Hadron epoch. There were also mesons, the result of quarks and antiquarks coming together. By the end of the epoch, the universe had cooled to a point (around 10^{10} K) at which neutrinos could no longer interact with matter. They took off on their own, whizzing around the universe and having no further interactions, and they are still doing that.

Seconds out

The Hadron epoch ended about one second after the Big Bang. In that first second, six epochs had passed; the four fundamental forces had separated out; quarks and leptons had sprung into existence, and some had stuck together to make the first baryons; many of those baryons had annihilated one another in matter–antimatter collisions; the temperature had fallen from over 10^{32} K to 10^{10} K and the size of the universe had expanded from smaller than a quark to larger than our solar system. It was a busy first second.

Leptons rule

The next epoch, by far the longest thus far, lasted from the end of the first second until about the end of the tenth – nine whole seconds! This was the Lepton epoch. After

most of the protons and antiprotons had mutually destructed, most of the mass of the universe was concentrated in leptons (electrons, muons, taus and their corresponding neutrinos). These, too, appeared as both leptons and antileptons. They continued to be produced until the end of the Lepton epoch. At that point, the temperature had dropped to a mere one billion (10^9) K and leptons could no longer be produced.

The leptons and antileptons annihilated one another. Electrons and antielectrons (usually called positrons) cancelled one another out; as a result, there were approximately the same number of

ANTI-ATOMS

There is nothing in the laws of physics to prevent antiparticles combining in the same way as the corresponding particles. This means an antiproton and a positron can come together to produce a hydrogen anti-atom. In theory, it would be possible to make anti-molecules of all kinds of anti-chemicals, even DNA, and build them up into anti-trees, anti-zebras, anti-planets, and so on. In practice it's very difficult to make and sustain antimatter, and the largest particle produced so far is a helium anti-nucleus. But maybe in another universe antimatter predominates.

electrons as protons. As the Lepton epoch progressed, construction and destruction went both ways, with gamma photons producing electron–positron pairs (as well as resulting from their demise). Heavier leptons were also produced but by the end of the epoch had decayed into electrons and positrons, neutrinos and antineutrinos.

These matter–antimatter annihilations produced a lot of spare energy. When a proton and an antiproton, or an electron and a positron, collide and destroy each other, their mass is released as energy (following Einstein's equation, $E=mc^2$), in a mix of photons and neutrinos. Consequently, by the end of the Lepton epoch there were about a billion photons for every proton or neutron.

Photons afoot

When the annihilations were over, the universe was a seething mass of protons, neutrons, electrons and highly energetic gamma photons. This was the Photon epoch, which lasted about three minutes. As the photons whizzed around at high speed, they frequently collided with electrons. This caused the electrons to vibrate, emitting a different photon in a different direction. Photons were scattering off electrons in all directions. Consequently they were not streaming through space as beams of light, as they do when you shine a light into clear air. Instead the universe was opaque; it was like shining a torch into a bank of fog.

Nuclear age

By the end of the Photon epoch, the temperature had cooled sufficiently so that protons and neutrons could come

On a foggy day, there's as much light as usual but we can't see it because the air is opaque – photons bounce around between water molecules. During the Photon epoch, they bounced off electrons in a similar way.

together and stay together. This was the Nucleosynthesis epoch, when the first atomic nuclei (besides hydrogen) were produced. It lasted about 17 minutes.

A proton is the nucleus of a hydrogen atom. When a proton and a neutron come together, they make heavy hydrogen, or deuterium. This still has a charge of +1, as the neutron has no charge, but it has twice the mass of a normal hydrogen nucleus. (Normal hydrogen is called protium.) Deuterium was the first step in building matter other than hydrogen in a process called nucleosynthesis.

HEAVY HYDROGEN

Deuterium was discovered and named in 1931 by American physical chemist Harold Urey. He found it the year before the discovery of the neutron, though, so its structure remained briefly obscure. Soon after discovering deuterium, Urey and others produced samples of 'heavy water' in which the deuterium content had been highly concentrated.

Most atomic nuclei besides hydrogen are made in stars, but deuterium is an exception. Most of the deuterium in existence was made during the first 20 minutes of the universe's life. In fact, deuterium is destroyed in the hearts of stars faster than it is produced, so the amount is probably decreasing.

Harold Urey won the Nobel Prize in Chemistry in 1934 for his discovery of deuterium.

Nucleosynthesis barely even paused at deuterium. At first the universe was so hot that the average energy of each particle was higher than the weak bonding energy holding the neutrons and protons together. This meant that no sooner was a particle of deuterium formed than it tore itself apart again. This 'deuterium bottleneck' lasted a few minutes, until the universe cooled enough for deuterium to form and remain intact. But deuterium is not very stable. If two deuterium nuclei came together and stuck, they formed a helium nucleus, with two protons and two neutrons. Most of the deuterium that formed immediately fused into helium. By the end of the epoch, there were only about 26 atoms of deuterium to every million atoms of protium. This is the ratio still found in gas giants such as Saturn.

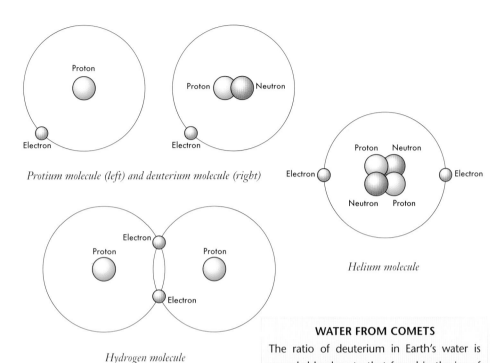

Protium molecule (left) and deuterium molecule (right)

Helium molecule

Hydrogen molecule

WATER FROM COMETS

The ratio of deuterium in Earth's water is remarkably close to that found in the ice of many comets, giving support to the theory that much of it was delivered by comets early in Earth's history.

Getting ahead

Most of the material produced by the end of the Nucleosynthesis epoch was present as hydrogen and helium. There was also the next element in the Periodic Table, lithium, and a tiny amount of beryllium. All four elements were present in extra isotopes (nuclei with different numbers of neutrons): He-3 (helium with two protons but only one neutron, rather than two), Li-7 (lithium with four rather than three neutrons), Be-7 (beryllium with three rather than four neutrons), and a tiny amount of an unstable isotope of hydrogen called tritium (with one proton and two neutrons).

The heavier elements (and most lithium and beryllium) were created very much later. Luckily, the huge surplus of protons meant that there would be plenty to work with when the time came.

By the end of the Nucleosynthesis epoch all the atomic nuclear material that was ever going to be made already existed. Some of the nuclei would later combine into heavier elements, but the universe was now in full possession of all its basic matter. The protons and neutrons in every atom of your body and in everything around you already existed by the time the universe was just 17 minutes old.

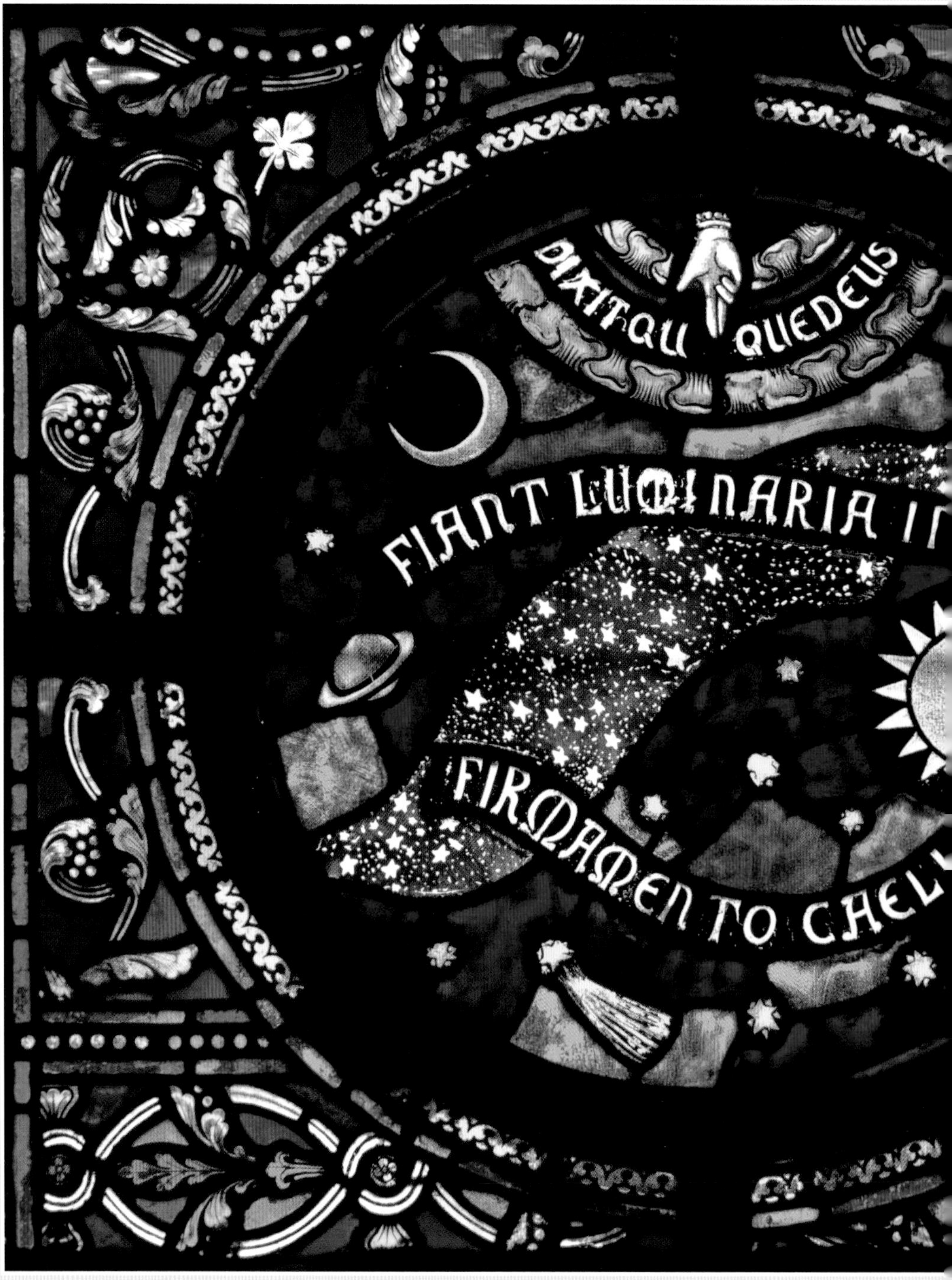
FIANT LUMINARIA
FIRMAMENTO

DARKNESS VISIBLE

'No light, but rather darkness visible.'

John Milton, *Paradise Lost*, Book 1

Far from looking like a big fiery explosion, as traditionally depicted, the Big Bang was not visible at all (even if there had been beings with eyes to see it). The photons produced in the first seconds were trapped, bouncing backwards and forwards, and didn't escape for 379,000 years.

'And God said: Let there be light – and there was light.' The Old Testament story of the Creation is rendered in stained glass at the Eglise Notre-Dame, Dinant, Belgium.

A cosmic battle

At the same time as the nuclei of the lighter elements were forming during nucleosynthesis, another epoch was beginning. Nucleosynthesis overlaps with the Photon epoch. The earliest epochs lasted a fraction of a second, and nucleosynthesis, at around 17 minutes, looks almost infinitely long by comparison. The Photon epoch lasted from around 10 seconds until 379,000 years – about a trillion times longer than all the previous epochs added together.

Although all the atomic nuclei were fixed by the end of the Nucleosynthesis epoch, the balance of energy and matter in the universe was still very much in favour of energy. Most of the baryons and a good deal of the leptons that appeared had been annihilated by encounters with their corresponding anti-particles, producing a large surplus of photons and neutrinos. There had previously been about a billion photons for each nucleon (proton or neutron); now some of the nucleons had combined, the ratio was even more in favour of photons.

Most of the mass of the system was in photons, their tiny mass more than made up for by their huge numbers.

Losing energy

The universe was still expanding, so photons and matter (nucleons) became ever more

---

MATTER AND ENERGY

Albert Einstein's equation $E=mc^2$ tells us that mass and energy are interchangeable. In the equation, E is energy, m is mass, and c is the speed of light. The energy of a fragment of matter is equal to its mass times the speed of light squared (which is a very large number). This is how much energy would be released by completely destroying the matter, ripping its atoms apart. This is possible because ultimately the particles that make up matter are little blobs or clouds, or strings, of energy. We don't think of a table as made of energy, we think of it as matter. But its constituent atoms are reducible to energy. When scientists talk about the energy:matter ratio of the universe, they mean the stuff that is pure energy, not tied up in any matter, set against the stuff we think of as matter – that which has extension in space, whether as a proton or as a train, moon, tree or cloud of gas.

Albert Einstein's famous equation from his special relativity theory yields the startling insight that matter and energy are essentially the same thing.

spread out. As the universe expanded, the wavelength of the photons stretched; this, in turn, reduced their energy. It's the same redshift effect we see when light is emitted by an object that is moving away from us (see page 21). Expansion of space has no equivalent impact on matter.

At some time around 70,000 years after the Big Bang, expansion had cost the photons so much energy that the balance tipped in favour of matter. The balance shifted again, about 5–6 billion years ago, so now energy – most specifically, dark energy – predominates once more (see page 196).

Ironically, a universe full of photons was dark. The plasma of matter scattered the photons, bouncing them around between particles in much the same way that fog scatters light, with the result that the universe was opaque. The universe was still too hot, and the photon bombardment too unrelenting, for colliding nuclei and electrons to get together. High-energy impacts just had them bouncing apart again.

Making atoms and light

The universe continued expanding and cooling, the wavelength of photons continued to reduce, and their energy levels dropped correspondingly. Finally, around 379,000 years after the Big Bang, the collisions between particles were no longer so energetic and at last atomic nuclei were able to capture and hold on to electrons. In this process, called recombination, the first atoms were created. At the same time, the universe became transparent as the photons could now stream through it unhindered. At this point, it was the size of the Milky Way and its temperature was around 3,000 K.

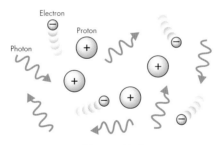

Before recombination

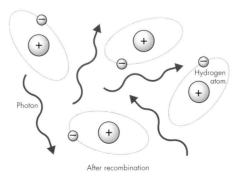

After recombination

As energy levels dropped, protons were able to capture and hold on to electrons, making hydrogen atoms.

Getting together

Protons have a positive charge and neutrons have no charge, so each atomic nucleus formed during nucleosynthesis had a positive charge equivalent to the number of protons it possessed. Hydrogen had a charge 1+, helium 2+, lithium 3+ and beryllium had a charge of 4+. There is no stable nucleus with five protons. This meant there was no way of making the jump to 6+ (carbon) and continuing with larger nuclei, so beryllium was the largest nucleus made by early nucleosynthesis.

All the electrons had an equal negative charge of -1. Although there is a natural electromagnetic attraction between the positive and negative matter, the collisions in the early universe were so energetic that particles just rebounded. As soon as the energy dropped sufficiently for the attraction to win out, the nuclei grabbed just the right number of electrons each to balance their positive charges, and the first atoms were born.

The atoms were now neutral – they had no charge. This meant that the photons no longer interacted strongly with them and were released, in a process known as photon decoupling, to go their own way. This was the end of the Photon epoch. It's also called the time of 'last scattering', as photons were no longer randomly scattered by the charged matter of the universe. They could move freely, and the universe became transparent. The released photons came to form the cosmic microwave background radiation (see page 58) which we can still examine today.

Electrons and more

As we have seen, J.J. Thomson discovered the first subatomic particle, the electron, in 1897. His model of the atom had electrons blobbed around randomly through a cloud of positive charge. It was soon overturned.

In 1909, the physicist Ernest Rutherford, originally from New Zealand, was working in Manchester, England, exploring radiation. He delegated the more tedious parts of his research to Ernest Marsden, a doctoral student. Marsden was tasked with firing alpha particles produced

J. J. Thomson with his students at the Cavendish Laboratory, Cambridge, UK. Ernest Rutherford is fourth from the left in the second row; Thomson sits with his arms folded in the middle of the front row.

by the radioactive decay of radium through a vacuum on to a thin sheet of gold foil and tracking their paths. Astonishingly, he found a tiny proportion of particles was deflected by very large angles and some even bounced straight back. According to Thomson's model of the atom, this was completely impossible. The diffuse cloud of positive charge could not produce such a strong repellent force. The only conclusion was that the model must be wrong.

Rutherford constructed a new model of the atom in which all the positive charge was concentrated in a very small centre (the nucleus); the electrons were outside this, orbiting at some distance, so most of the atom was empty space. The few alpha particles that came too close to the positively charged nucleus would be deflected. The rest passed straight through the empty space of the atom. Rutherford published his discovery of the presence of protons in the nucleus in 1919, though

he published his initial findings in 1911. In 1913, Danish physicist Niels Bohr improved the model. He proposed that the electrons did not wander randomly around the nucleus but orbited in designated shells, or orbitals, just as planets revolve around a star in a fixed orbit.

A quantum leap

In the 1920s, the orbitals became linked to energy levels. The location of an electron in relation to the nucleus is constrained by the amount of energy it has. If it is supplied with more energy (from a photon) it can jump up a level to another orbital. If it drops a level, it releases energy, again in the form of a photon. This discovery turned out to be hugely important for interpreting the spectra of stars and other objects. The tiny jump from one orbital to another is called a quantum jump, or quantum leap. Contrary to popular usage, it is about the smallest step that it's possible to make.

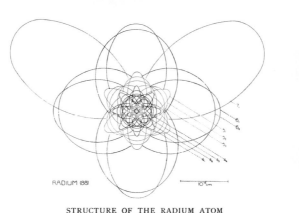

STRUCTURE OF THE RADIUM ATOM

Bohr's diagram of the structure of the radium atom from 1926 shows the different shapes of the orbitals of its 88 electrons.

The neutron

In 1932, English physicist James Chadwick discovered that the nucleus is also home to particles with no charge, called neutrons. The discovery of the neutron explained the difference between two numbers important in chemistry, atomic mass and atomic number. It also paved the way for harnessing nuclear power, because bombarding atoms with neutrons can blast them apart, releasing immense quantities of energy.

In 1932, James Chadwick discovered the neutron using this small ionization chamber. It detected protons blasted out of paraffin wax by a beam of neutrons generated by irradiating beryllium.

Cosmic waves in the background

The decoupling of photons meant they were free to rush off in all directions. This sudden outburst of energy is, if anything is, the 'flash' of the Big Bang. It just had to wait nearly 380,000 years to escape.

The expansion and cooling of the universe didn't stop at this point, of course. As the photons moved, space continued to expand between them and the universe continued to cool. Just as expanding space lengthened the wavelength of the photons

before decoupling, it has continued to do so ever since. The photons now have the wavelength of microwave radiation. They are spread through the observable universe, and presumably beyond, and form the CMB which is effectively a 'fossil' of the early energy state of the universe, the afterglow of the Big Bang. It is now 'brightest' at a wavelength of around 2 mm (microwave size); visible light has a wavelength 4,000 times shorter. It will continue to lengthen to the point at which it will eventually (far in the future) no longer be detectable at all.

WHY THERE IS CMB

It might seem strange that the CMB is still there to be observed. After all, if we drop a stone into a pool of water the ripples don't freeze, waiting to be observed years later. But a pool is not the whole universe. The energy of the Big Bang had nowhere to go because there is no 'elsewhere'. When we drop a stone into a pool, the energy of the ripples can dissipate as there is plenty of 'not-pool' at the edges. The energy of the CMB is forever trapped in the universe. The photons are still all around us: there are about 400 CMB photons in every cubic centimetre of space.

Discovering CMB

The CMB was discovered accidentally in 1964, but had been predicted nearly 20 years earlier. While working on the synthesis of elements after the Big Bang, Ralph Alpher (see page 23), proposed and later calculated the relic radiation that might still be found. Working with Robert Herman, he realized that the radiation should by that point in time show at a temperature of around 5 K. Alpher and Herman published their result in 1948, but no one was sufficiently convinced to look for the radiation.

As we have seen, the CMB was found by two radio astronomers, Arno Penzias and Robert Wilson, who were not in fact looking for it. In 1964, they were working on cosmic radio waves using a new highly sensitive antenna intended to pick up radio signals being bounced off the first communications satellites. They encountered a lot of interference, with a louder-than-expected background signal. Penzias and Wilson eradicated all the possible sources of interference they could think of, but it continued. As they had eliminated all possible Earth-bound sources they concluded that the interference must be coming from the sky. Since it was the same day and night, summer and winter (therefore not related to the Earth's position in relation to the Sun), they decided the source was not within the solar system.

Penzias and Wilson at one point suspected the interference was caused by nesting pigeons and drove them all away, clearing up their droppings. But the CMB persisted.

THE UNIVERSE ON TV

At millimetre-wavelengths, the CMB is so bright that it contributes to the static of a de-tuned analogue television set. Part of the fuzzy snow-like image is picked up from the CMB and comes from the start of the universe. Not many people still have access to an analogue TV, but with a high-quality radio set you can still hear the Big Bang. About half a per cent of the static noise between clear signals is from the CMB – so you can de-tune your radio and listen to a little bit of the flash of light at the start of the universe, stretched so far that it is now just radio waves you are receiving as sound.

At the same time, three astrophysicists at nearby Princeton were preparing to search for the CMB. Robert Dicke, Jim Peebles and David Wilkinson hoped to find microwave relics of photon decoupling in exactly the area of the spectrum that was represented by Penzias and Wilson's mysterious signal. A professor of physics at MIT, Bernard Burke, saw a pre-print copy of their paper and told Penzias and Wilson, who realized that the predictions matched their interference and they might already have found the CMB. When the Princeton team visited the antenna they confirmed it was, indeed, the looked-for cosmic microwave signal. Both teams published their half of the story in the same issue of *The Astrophysical Journal* in 1965. The Penzias/Wilson paper was astonishingly understated, with the unenticing title 'A Measurement of Excess Antenna Temperature at 4080 Mc/s' and no direct mention of its significance. Even so, the *New York Times* ran the story as headline news before the journal article came out. In 1978, Penzias and Wilson received the Nobel Prize in physics for their work.

The identification of the CMB was one of the most significant scientific discoveries of all time. It was compelling evidence that the Big Bang model is correct. The massive flash produced by photon decoupling was released everywhere at the same time, which is why the CMB is all around us and has no directional source (the very feature that originally puzzled Penzias and Wilson). It has been carried through the expanding universe and, although the wavelength increases with inflation, the radiation will continue to be everywhere.

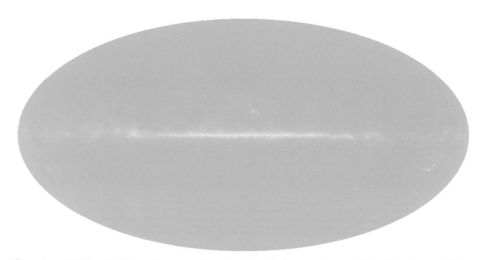

If Penzias and Wilson had been able to map the entire sky with their equipment, this is what they would have seen: uniformity. The grey band is where the plane of the Milky Way lies, obscuring the background radiation.

SPACE WAS PREVIOUSLY ORANGE

Space as we know it is black. The flash of light liberated by photon decoupling, however, was orange. This can be calculated from the temperature at the time, which was around 3,000 K. At this temperature most photons would be in the infrared range, but there would have been enough in the visible spectrum for the light to have looked orange (had we been there to see it). The cooling universe has elongated the wavelength of all the photons so that now there are no visible-light photons of CMB, and space looks black.

A lumpy universe

An important feature of the CMB is that it is astonishingly even throughout the sky. This is taken as evidence that the entire observable universe was originally uniform and much smaller. When it expanded, the uniformity remained; it just became more spread out. But the CMB is not entirely homogenous. There are small fluctuations reflected in variations in temperature. These correspond to slight variations in the original structure of the universe which have been magnified by expansion. Although these variations, caused by quantum irregularities before inflation, are tiny, they were enough to seed structures in the universe. The tiny variations led to expansion stopping at slightly different points. That in turn produced a marginally uneven distribution of radiation and matter, producing hot and cold spots. These variations could not even out after inflation because the speed of light became a limiting factor – they were too far apart for energy to move between them.

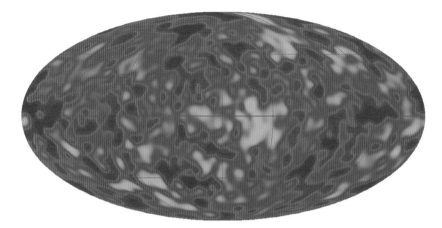

The first COBE map, from the initial two years' data.

Measuring the CMB

Measuring the CMB and finding its variations became an important task for astronomers. If Penzias and Wilson had been able to measure it across the entire sky, their map would have shown something entirely uniform. Mapping the entire sky with far greater accuracy than Penzias and Wilson had been able to was the task undertaken in 1989–96 by NASA's Cosmic Background Explorer satellite (COBE) COBE produced the first whole-sky map of the CMB. It found that the CMB has an almost perfect black-body spectrum but is not entirely uniform: there are very slight variations (anisotropies) in the radiation, corresponding to just one part in 100,000.

Two of the scientists responsible for the work, George Smoot and John Mather, were awarded the 2006 Nobel Prize in Physics. Their findings marked the beginning of cosmology as a precise science and sounded the death knell for the alternative steady-state model of the universe. They were entirely in accordance with predictions of what would occur in the case of the Big Bang.

After COBE

The next mission to map the CMB would be even more detailed. In 2001, the Wilkinson Microwave Anisotropy Probe (WMAP) was launched; its findings revolutionized our understanding of the universe and gave the first fine-scale map (to a resolution of 0.2 degrees across the sky) of the detailed structure of the CMB.

The most detailed map to date, however, was produced from data collected by the Planck mission, launched by the European Space Agency (ESA). Between 2009 and 2013, this observatory completed five full-sky scans, mapping the CMB with high sensitivity and small angular resolution. The crucial findings returned by WMAP and Planck are:

• the age of the universe is 13.77 billion years (WMAP) or 13.8 billion years (Planck)

• the distribution of variations in the CMB across the sky matches the predictions of the simplest model of inflation

The WMAP map, from nine years' data.

- normal atomic (baryonic) matter can only account for 4.6 per cent (WMAP) or 4.9 per cent (Planck) of the universe

- 'dark matter' (not made up of atoms) accounts for 24 per cent (WMAP) or 26.8 per cent (Planck) of the universe

- 71.4 per cent (WMAP) or 68.3 per cent (Planck) of the universe is accounted for by mysterious 'dark energy'

- the size of variations in the density of the universe is slightly larger at large scales than at small scales – a finding which supports the theory of cosmic inflation.

From lumps to galaxy clusters

The WMAP, Planck and earlier maps reveal that the tiny inequalities in the temperature of the CMB would, over the coming billions of years, lead to the massive structure of the universe. Areas of slightly higher temperature, and therefore greater energy, would become the focus of

THE SURFACE OF LAST SCATTERING

If we sit on or near Earth and measure the CMB coming at us from all directions, we are measuring photons that have taken between 12.1 and 13.4 billion years to get here from their starting points, depending on the age of the universe. Those arriving here precisely at this moment all have originating points that are equidistant from us, defining, in all probability, a spherical surface. This imaginary surface is called the 'surface of last scattering'.

gravitational collapse and would contain a concentration of matter and energy. These would eventually be the areas occupied by galaxy clusters.

The cooler areas would be the apparently barren spaces of the universe. However, at the point of photon decoupling these events were a long way in the future. The making of stars and galaxies would be the work of the next epoch.

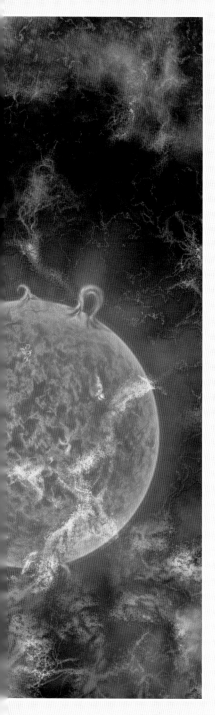

CHAPTER 4

STAR LIGHT, STAR BRIGHT

'See plastic Nature working to this end,
The single atoms each to other tend,
Attract, attracted to, the next in place
Formed and impelled its neighbour to embrace.
See matter next, with various life endued,
Press to one centre still, the general good.'

Alexander Pope,
An Essay on Man, 1734

Produced by condensing clouds of hydrogen and helium, the first stars formed about 180 million years after the Big Bang. The large-scale structure of the universe was put in place at the same time. It was beginning to be the place that is familiar to us now.

An artist's impression of one of the very first stars, glowing blue. Made entirely of hydrogen and helium, they were surrounded in space by more hydrogen.

In 2019, a tiny radio spectrometer the size of a table detected the fingerprint of hydrogen absorbing radiation at a particular wavelength from the background of space. The equipment was set up in the desert of Western Australia, far from all sources of radio interference. It confirmed that the first stars burst into life 180 million years after the Big Bang, ending the Dark Ages of the universe.

Into the darkness

The burst of light of photon decoupling was followed by an era of utter darkness, sometimes called the cosmic Dark Ages. Any short-wavelength radiation that might have been emitted was quickly absorbed by the gas spread throughout the universe. We can only theorize about what might have been going on during the cosmic Dark Ages using computer simulations based on what we know of the time that came after. During the Dark Ages, the universe somehow changed from the remarkably homogeneous, smooth universe fossilized in the CMB to one that is highly structured, with areas of very high density of matter and areas that are virtually empty.

Pulling together

Our best theory for what happened gives gravity a starring role. The tiny irregularities we can see preserved in the CMB became the focus of accumulating matter. Gravity attracted other matter and energy to the areas where there was already slightly more. The result was that some areas had enough concentrated matter all pulling towards itself with ever greater force that the very first stars began to form, probably at some time around 150–180 million years after the Big Bang.

Revealing gravity

For a long time, the notion that some kind of attractive force operates between matter has been obvious from everyday experience. Gravity was first outlined as an attractive force that prevents things from falling off the Earth by Indian mathematician Brahmagupta (AD *c.*598–*c.*668) who used the term *gurutvakarshan*, meaning 'to be attracted by the master.' An earlier Indian astronomer and mathematician, Varahamihira (AD 505–587), had said there might be some force which prevents objects from flying off the Earth and keeps the heavenly bodies in their correct positions, but he hadn't given it a name.

GALILEO VINDICATED

Commander David Scott of the Apollo 15 mission to the Moon in 1971 demonstrated that Galileo was right – objects do fall at the same speed if air resistance is removed. Scott dropped a metal hammer and a feather taken from a falcon called Baggins at the same time. Both hit the surface of the Moon simultaneously.

The first person to set about investigating gravity was Italian scientist Galileo Galilei (1564–1642). He contested a claim made by Aristotle that heavier objects fall more rapidly than light objects. He (possibly) carried out a demonstration which involved dropping balls from the top of the Leaning Tower of Pisa to prove that objects of the same shape but different mass reach the ground at the same time. He correctly suggested that objects fall at different speeds because of air resistance, not gravity. Whether or not the Leaning Tower was involved, Galileo certainly tested the action of gravity by rolling balls down a slope.

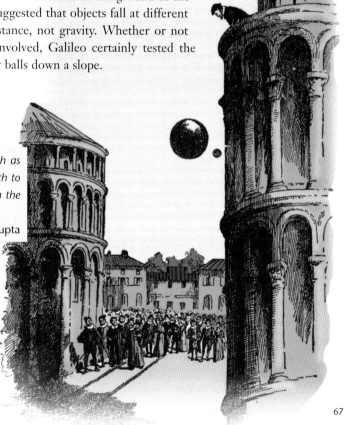

'Bodies fall towards the Earth as it is in the nature of the Earth to attract bodies, just as it is in the nature of water to flow.'

Brahmagupta

A later imagining of Galileo dropping a cannonball and another spherical object from the Leaning Tower of Pisa.

Keeping the planets in place

Galileo's work prepared the ground for the more famous work of Isaac Newton. Born in 1642, the year Galileo died, Newton set out the first mathematical formulation of gravity in his most important work, *Philosophiæ Naturalis Principia Mathematica*, published in 1687. Another probably apocryphal tale describes Newton being hit on the head by a falling fruit while sitting under an apple tree. The experience inspired him to investigate the force that compels the apple to fall to the ground. His inverse square law of universal gravitation states that the gravitational force *F* acting between two objects is given by the formula:

$$F = G \; \frac{m_1 \, m_2}{r^2}$$

where m_1 and m_2 are the masses of the two objects, *r* is the distance between the centres of the two objects, and *G* is the gravitational constant. If the distance between two objects (say, a planet and its moon) doubles, the gravitational force will reduce by a factor of 4 (2^2). The force acts between the objects, but the effect is noticed most on the less massive object. That's why the apple falls to Earth more than the Earth rises to meet the apple.

> 'I deduced that the forces which keep the planets in their orbs must be reciprocally as the squares of their distances from the centres about which they revolve: and thereby compared the force requisite to keep the Moon in her orb with the force of gravity at the surface of the Earth; and found them answer pretty nearly.'
>
> Isaac Newton, 1687

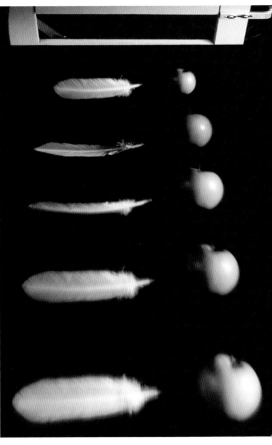

Newton's law of gravity demonstrated by a feather and an apple falling together in a vacuum chamber.

The best endorsement of Newton's theory of gravitation came when it was found that the observed orbit of the planet Uranus did not match its predicted behaviour. Astronomers thought another planet must be disturbing its orbit by the influence of its own gravitational force. John Couch Adams and Urbain Le Verrier independently predicted the location of a new planet, Neptune, using Newton's theory. The planet was found where it was expected to be in 1846.

The deformation of space-time by the gravity produced by a massive planet.

Gravity gets shapely

No one had much to add about gravity for more than 200 years after *Principia*. Then Albert Einstein reassessed it in his general theory of relativity, published in 1915. Instead of a force acting between two objects, Einstein described gravity as a distortion of space-time that occurs around objects with mass.

This can be illustrated by imagining dropping a heavy ball onto a blanket that has been pulled tight. The ball deforms the surface of the blanket, causing a dip into which it rolls. If a smaller ball is dropped onto the blanket, it will roll towards the large ball. It doesn't roll because the large ball is attracting it, but because the dip in the surface of the blanket compels it to do so. The distortion of space-time by massive objects is similar, but works in three-dimensional space rather than a two-dimensional blanket. Every object of mass causes some distortion of space-time, although small objects don't have as great an effect as more massive ones.

Most objects adhere to Isaac Newton's model of gravity, but there are a few cases where it doesn't apply; these can be described by Einstein's formulation and the associated equations.

Bending light

A particularly important finding was that gravity can affect light. Our usual understanding is that light travels in a straight line, but this requires us to define what a straight line is. On a flat plane, it is the shortest distance between two points, and parallel straight lines never meet or diverge. But on a curved surface, such as a sphere, the shortest distance between two points is a geodesic – part of a great circle, like the equator around the Earth. We are more likely to think of the equator as a curve than a straight line.

When gravity deforms space-time, light or other electromagnetic radiation takes the shortest path, but that shortest path is through a curve so it is not really a 'straight line'.

The telescope used for observing the eclipse of 1919 from Brazil on Eddington's expedition.

Einstein predicted that light from a distant star would follow a path distorted by the Sun's gravitational field. He deduced that this would mean the star would appear deflected by 1.75 seconds of arc (about a thousandth the width of the full moon). Newton's theory also had light deflected by gravity, but to a lesser degree, only 0.86 seconds. There are few opportunities to test this as we can't usually see stars that are close to the Sun. But we can see them when there is a total eclipse and the Sun is darkened during the day. In 1919, Arthur Eddington led an expedition to test the prediction by measuring the apparent position of a star near the Sun during an eclipse. The position of the star was measured from two locations, one in Brazil and the other on Principe, an island off the west coast of Africa. The results confirmed Einstein's prediction and were widely accepted as proof of the theory of general relativity.

BAD LUCK WITH ECLIPSES

Eclipses turn up reliably, but they are not reliably observable. The earliest attempt to test Einstein's idea was thwarted even before he had published it. The German physicist Erwin Finlay-Freundlich of the Berlin Observatory led an expedition to Crimea in 1914 to observe a total solar eclipse. Unfortunately World War I broke out, and he was arrested as a German spy before the eclipse took place.

William W. Campbell led a team from the Lick Observatory in California to Crimea, but it rained and the eclipse was not visible. Campbell's special eclipse-camera was impounded by the Russians (who might have been puzzled by this sudden war-time interest in eclipses) and not returned until it was too late for him to take it to the next eclipse, expected in Venezuela in 1916, nor the following one in Washington State in 1918. These mishaps meant the prize was still there for Eddington to claim in 1919. But it rained in Principe, so he only managed to take a few good photographs. Nor did the expedition have much success in Brazil, where Eddington captured out-of-focus, blurred images when the clouds cleared just momentarily.

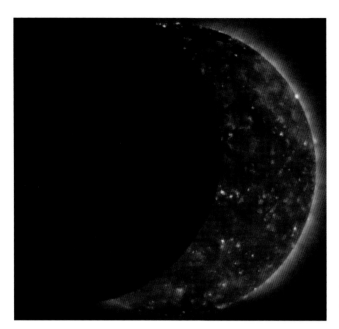

An eclipse of the Sun observed from the satellite Hinode in 2009.

Building a framework

Gravity's role in forming the structure of the universe was crucial as it magnified the tiny fluctuations in the density of matter. The idea that these variations, or anisotropies, accumulated matter and became the basis of the large-scale structure of the present universe emerged soon after the discovery of the CMB, but ran into trouble during the 1970s.

Galaxies don't add up

If astronomers focused only on the baryonic (that is, normal) matter in the universe, they could not account for its current structure and the development of galaxies. In the early 1980s, astronomers found that if they added cold, dark matter to the early universe in high enough proportions, the problem could be overcome. 'Dark matter', as its name suggests, is a shady substance. No one is very sure what it is. It is certainly 'matter' because it has mass and interacts with gravity, but it's not normal matter. It's 'dark' because it doesn't reflect light or interact with other forms of electromagnetic radiation, so it can't be detected directly. By 'cold' astronomers mean that it is moving at speeds slower than the speed of light.

There are good reasons for supposing dark matter exists even though it's invisible to all forms of radiation. If you imagine wrapping a magnet in a dark cloth and placing it on a table, then dropping iron filings around it, you would be able to tell from the movement of the iron filings that there is a magnetic field present, even though you can't see the magnet. Similarly, the impact of the gravity produced by dark matter can be seen, even though we can't see the matter itself.

Dark matter is the only way of explaining the speed at which stars at the edge of a galaxy move. The stars rotate faster than they should do, if the total mass of the galaxy was just the mass of its visible matter. They behave as though the galaxy has much greater mass than is apparent. They could only move as they do if there is something else, something we can't see, contributing to its mass. A 'halo' of dark matter around the galaxy would keep the visible matter in place and prevent the galaxy from being torn apart.

Adding dark matter

Astronomers discovered that if they assumed that only 5 per cent of matter was normal baryonic matter and the other 95 per cent was dark matter, the mathematics could be made to work to form galaxies and galaxy clusters. This was the cold dark matter (CDM) model. Even so, astronomical observations in 1988–90 showed that more galaxy clustering was found than the model predicted. In 1992, the results from COBE revealed the level of anisotropies in the CMB, giving a further mismatch with the model. Astronomers began to try out different variants of the CDM model, including mixed hot and cold dark matter.

With the discovery in 1998 that the rate of expansion of the universe is increasing, it was possible to refine the CDM model in a version called Lambda-CDM (ΛCDM). The eleventh letter of the Greek alphabet, lambda (Λ) stands for a cosmological constant, a figure representing the energy density of empty space. This is known as dark energy, and is thought to be the force that acts against gravity to drive the expansion of the universe (see page 196).

This Hubble Space Telescope image shows an enormous cluster of galaxies 2.2 billion light years away. Dark matter cannot be photographed, so its distribution is shown using a blue overlay.

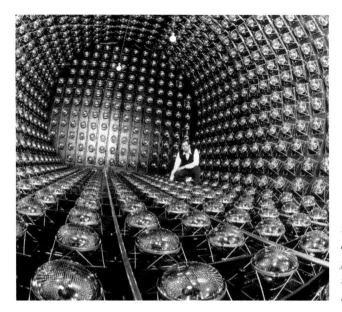

Photomultiplier tubes (PMTs) in a neutrino detector detect the tiny flash of light produced when a neutrino (see page 74) strikes the liquid core of the detector.

Since the start of the 21st century, further observations and measurements of the CMB have supported the model, which is now considered accurate to within 1 per cent. It sounds like a success story – and it is – except we still don't know what the 'cold dark matter' is or how it came into being. The tests to discover the answer to this question continue.

Nothing to see here

The idea of dark matter was first mentioned by Lord Kelvin in 1884. Having calculated the mass of the galaxy by looking at the speeds of different stars moving around its centre, Kelvin concluded that there is more mass than we can account for with visible objects, and so 'many of our stars, perhaps a great majority of them, may be dark bodies'. But while there may be many 'dark stars' and other bodies we can't see, there is not enough hidden normal matter of this kind to account for the huge matter-deficit of the universe.

The first suggestion that the quantity of dark matter might be calculated from its gravitational effect was made by Dutch astronomer Jacobus Kapteyn in 1922. Jan Oort also talked of it in 1932, again as a way of reconciling the missing mass of the galaxy. Fritz Zwicky made the same calculation in 1933: working on the Coma cluster of around 1,000 galaxies, he estimated its mass at 400 times greater than the mass of visible matter in the galaxies, suggesting that hidden matter was holding the cluster together.

In 1980, American astronomer Vera Rubin showed that most galaxies must contain about six times as much dark matter as visible matter. This corresponds roughly with the current calculations from the CMB that just under 5 per cent of the universe is visible matter, nearly 27 per cent is dark matter and the rest is dark energy.

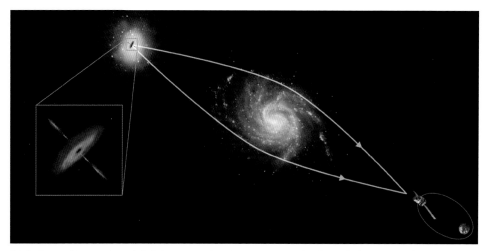

Light from a distant galaxy, left, is bent around an intervening spiral galaxy which acts like a lens. The result, gravitational lensing, means that details can be seen which could not otherwise be visible through a telescope.

Dark matter is not antimatter. If it was, it would be annihilated on contact with matter and wouldn't exist to be observed. And dark matter can't be black holes because large black holes bend any radiation that approaches them, creating an effect called gravitational lensing. There are not enough lensing events for dark matter to be hiding as black holes. The best suggestions so far are that dark matter could perhaps be neutrinos, axions or neutralinos.

Neutrinos were first proposed in 1930 by Wolfgang Pauli and detected in 1955 by Clyde Cowan and Frederick Reines. At first they were thought to be massless, but in 1998 one type of neutrino was found to have a very low mass. There are lots of neutrinos, but their mass is so tiny it would still be hard for them to account for all the dark matter. In 1977, theorized particles known as axions were proposed to solve a complex problem in quantum mechanics. There is so far no evidence of the existence

NEUTRINOS

Neutrinos are uncharged leptons which otherwise resemble the charged ones – electrons, muons and tau. Because a neutrino (so named because it is electrically neutral) doesn't interact with matter, it is extremely difficult to detect even though neutrinos are thought to be the most numerous particles in the universe. They are tracked in detectors situated deep underground to avoid interference (as they don't interact with matter, they have no difficulty travelling through Earth to the detectors). At the Sudbury Neutrino Observatory, a tank containing 1,000 tons of heavy water is bombarded by a trillion neutrinos a second, but only 30 neutrinos a day are actually detected.

of axions; if they do exist, they would have small mass but would have been produced in large numbers during the Big Bang. Neutralinos have been described, but all attempts to find evidence of their existence has failed. The favoured explanation at present is that dark matter probably consists of a type (or types) of particle we haven't yet discovered.

A vast sponge

The ΛCDM model gives a coherent account of how the large-scale structure of the universe developed. Whatever the nature of dark matter, it drew together at points of slightly greater density in the universe – the anisotropies in the CMB. Dark matter congealed into clumps and filaments which formed the superstructure of the

universe, something like a vast sponge with filaments and walls surrounding areas of emptier space. Where dark matter was denser, the increased gravity of these areas pulled in the hydrogen and helium (normal baryonic matter). As the density of matter at these points increased, its gravitational attraction for other matter also increased and the concentration of matter around the framework accelerated. Empty areas became emptier and denser areas became denser. Eventually the first stars and galaxies formed at the points of densest matter.

In 2017 astronomers set up a computer simulation which replicates conditions in the universe before the formation of the first galaxy clusters. The Evolution and Assembly of GaLaxies and their Environments (EAGLE) simulation was

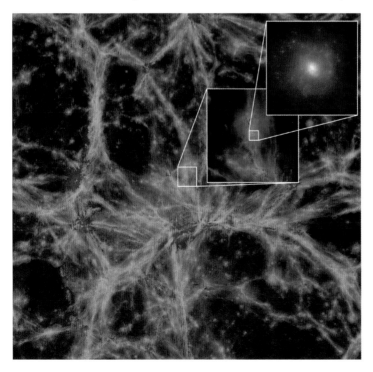

Produced by the EAGLE project, this supercomputer simulation shows part of the universe's superstructure. The colour-coding relates to temperature, with red the hottest and blue the coldest. The insets zoom in on a galaxy the same shape as the Milky Way.

The James Webb Telescope, scheduled for launch in 2021, will use infrared to search for the earliest stars. The light from these long-dead stars will have redshifted beyond the visible spectrum into the infrared spectrum.

large enough to contain 10,000 galaxies the size of the Milky Way.

Making stars

At the densest points in the network of filaments of matter, stars began to coalesce. We don't know much about the first stars that formed, but we can deduce the method of their formation.

The birth of a star

The process by which a cloud of condensing hydrogen gas becomes first a proto-star and then a star was described by English astronomer and mathematician James Jeans (1877–1946) who, with Eddington, was one of the founders of British cosmology. He studied the dynamics of gases and applied them to nebulae in the early 1900s.

Jeans found that a cloud of gas will be in equilibrium if the pressure of particles moving within it is equal to the pressure of gravity pulling the atoms towards one another. The mass of a cloud that is in equilibrium is called the Jeans mass. If anything disturbs a gas cloud in equilibrium – perhaps a greater density of gas in one small area – it has a domino effect. The denser area has a greater gravitational attraction for nearby atoms, so more gas moves into it, increasing the gravity further. It triggers gravitational collapse, with outward pressure no longer able to counterbalance the pull of gravity. This process fuels the birth of stars now just as it did at the very beginning of the first star-building epoch.

The critical size of a gas cloud that tips it over into collapse is called the Jeans length: once the cloud reaches this radius, collapse is inevitable. The Jeans instability, the point at which collapse is triggered, is a function of the size, temperature and pressure within a gas cloud. As more and more hydrogen is drawn together, the pressure and temperature of the gas increases until the tipping point is reached. This explains how a star forms as a super-dense cloud of

PROPOSING EARLY STARS

The notion that the first stars differed from the current generation of stars dates from 1978, but developed from work done in 1944 when Austrian-American astronomer Walter Baade distinguished two classes or populations of stars based on differences that correspond to their age (see page 95). He found that the older stars contained a higher proportion of hydrogen and helium than the newer stars, which showed more diversity of composition. Baade labelled the newer stars Population I and the older stars Population II.

This begged the question of where the heavier elements were coming from. As we shall see, they are mostly manufactured within stars and at the ends of the lives of stars. For there to be any of these heavier elements, they must have been made in or by previous stars. The very first stars, with no other elements available, must have been made entirely of hydrogen and helium from the primordial matter of the universe. In 1978, a new hypothetical class of Population III stars was added to Baade's system. No Population III star has ever been observed, but it seems hard to avoid them as a stage in the story of the universe. These first-generation stars made the first heavier elements that the Big Bang could not produce.

The dwarf galaxy ESO 553-46 produces stars at a very rapid rate. The new stars are glowing blueish-white here while heating the surrounding gas, which glows red. These stars contain little more than hydrogen and helium, making them very similar to the first stars in the universe.

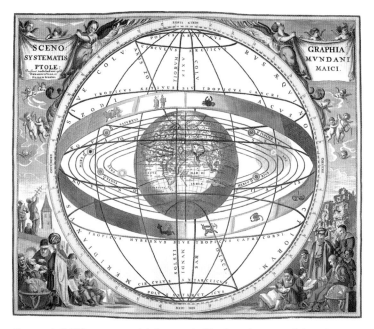

For nearly 2,000 years, a model that put the Earth at the centre of the universe persisted, stifling possible progress in cosmology and astronomy.

gas, but not how it produces energy. This puzzle would be worked out during the first half of the 20th century.

Superstars

The very earliest stars contained only the hydrogen and helium that had been formed in early nucleosynthesis. In this they differ considerably from later stars, which would have contained more ingredients. Many of the first stars grew to be 60 to 300 times the size of the Sun and some even larger than the stars that followed billions of years later. They were very energetic and probably burnt themselves out in millions of years or less. (The Sun will last another five billion years.) In other respects, these early stars worked in the same way as the stars around us now.

The mechanism of the stars

Astronomers have found out how stars work by considering Earth's own star, the Sun. Although it is of a much later generation, the lessons learnt by considering it almost certainly apply to the earliest stars.

The enquiry began with the ancients, who first looked up at the Sun and pondered its ability to produce heat and light. The Greek philosopher Anaxagoras suggested 2,500 years ago that the Sun is a fiery rock and the stars are the same. He said the only reason the Sun shines so brightly and that we can feel its heat is because it's much closer to us than the other stars. This moment of clarity was soon eclipsed by less enlightened models. Religion taught that humans are special and their place in the heavens is central. Instead of one of many equal fiery bodies, the Sun became subservient to the Earth, just another orb in its trailing entourage along with the Moon and planets. It wasn't until 1838 that it was found that the Sun is a star like any other.

As long as people were content to believe the Sun is a heavenly light, kept burning by divine power, there was no problem. A deity doesn't need to explain how a star burns; science, on the other hand, does. If the Sun is to follow the normal rules of science it must have a source of energy. It must also have enough energy to have lasted at least as long as the Earth has existed. The first questions for the ancients, therefore, were – How old is the Earth? And how long must the Sun have been burning already?

Six thousand years – and counting

Aristotle believed that Earth, like all the universe, had existed forever and would exist eternally. The Roman philosopher-poet Lucretius thought the Earth might have started little earlier than the Trojan wars, the earliest event known to him. Archaeological evidence now suggests that the Trojan wars ended around 1180 BC, which would make the Earth not much more than 1,000 years old at the time of Lucretius.

Early Christian and Talmudic tradition attempted to date the Earth by working back through the genealogies recorded in the sacred texts. Most famously, in 1650, the Primate of all Ireland, James Ussher, came up with the date of 22 October 4004 BC (with a corresponding end date of around AD 2000, which we have happily passed without incident). An approximate Earth age of 6,000 years was generally considered about right. Less than 200 years ago, most people in the western world still believed the Earth was only a few thousand years old.

James Ussher famously calculated the date of Creation in Christian tradition, though he was not the only or first person to do so.

HOW OLD?

Today there is a clean split between scientists and Creationists, but this wasn't always the case. The religious method for dating Earth was widely accepted around the time Ussher came up with his figure of 22 October 4004 BC. Renowned scientists such as Johannes Kepler and Isaac Newton also calculated Earth's age using the same method. Kepler came up with the date 3992 BC. and Isaac Newton may have plumped for 4000 BC.

A more robust approach to working out Earth's age began with the advent of geological dating in the 1660s. By the late 19th century, the general consensus was that Earth is around 100 million years old. The Sun, then, would need a source of energy that has lasted for at least 100 million years.

The heat of the Sun

The first assumption, that the Sun has some form of fuel which was burned to produce

The heat of the Sun is so immediately apparent that the idea it is burning suggests itself readily.

heat, could not explain its longevity. If the Sun were a vast lump of coal, it must surely burn itself out after a while. A more enterprising suggestion, originally made by German physicist Julius von Mayer (1814–78), was that the Sun was powered by meteors crashing into it. The meteors would have had to keep up a formidable rate of impacts and there was no evidence to suggest there were enough passing meteors, nor that the Sun was increasing in mass, as it must inevitably have had to do under such a sustained onslaught. Furthermore the Sun's increasing mass would have been immediately evident in changes to the orbits of the planets. These were considerable problems for Mayer's model.

The physicist Lord Kelvin (William Thomson) suggested that the energy of the Sun came first from the kinetic energy of the moving material that formed it, crushed together by gravity. As it cooled, it shrank, gravity pulling it together further, and making it 'merely an incandescent liquid mass cooling'. While Kelvin didn't rule out the possibility that the Sun was 'created as an active source of heat at some time of not immeasurable antiquity, by an overruling decree', he described this as 'in the highest degree improbable'.

In the explanation favoured by Kelvin, meteors were again the raw material of the Sun, but this time as a myriad small bodies drawn together by gravity and yielding their previously kinetic energy as heat. This interpretation was made possible by work carried out by German physicist Hermann von Helmholtz on the conservation of energy. In 1847, von Helmholtz drew together heat, light, electricity and magnetism to treat them as a single 'force' (we would now call them forms of energy). He argued that this force (energy) can change form, but is not added or created in a closed system. This model allowed Kelvin to assert that the kinetic energy of the moving meteors converts to the heat energy released by the Sun.

Kelvin's assessment was based on contemporary calculations of the surface temperature of the Sun and the amount of heat it radiates each year, and on the supposition that the Sun is similar in composition to the Earth ('we also have excellent reason for believing that the sun's substance is very much like the earth's.') He concluded that the Sun's diameter must shrink around a tenth of a per cent in every 20,000 years, that the Sun must have been providing heat for less than 100 million years and that it would have been hotter in the past than it is now.

'The sun and his heat . . . have originated in a coalition of smaller bodies, falling together by mutual gravitation, and generating, as they must do according to the great law demonstrated by Joule, an exact equivalent of heat for the motion lost in collision.'

Lord Kelvin, 1862

William Thomson is most famous for his work on thermodynamics. He was the first British scientist to be ennobled, becoming Lord Kelvin in 1866.

81

'It seems, therefore, on the whole most probable that the sun has not illuminated the earth for 100,000,000 years, and almost certain that he has not done so for 500,000,000 years. As for the future, we may say, with equal certainty, that inhabitants of the earth cannot continue to enjoy the light and heat essential to their life for many million years longer unless sources now unknown to us are prepared in the great storehouse of creation.'

Lord Kelvin, 1862

New forms of energy

There were still several crucial discoveries to be made before scientists could work out what powered the Sun. The first step was the discovery of radioactivity, made by French physicist Henri Becquerel in 1896. By accident he found that salts of uranium emit a form of radiation that registers on a photographic plate. Becquerel was testing his theory that a compound of uranium (potassium uranyl sulfate) would absorb energy from sunlight and then emit the energy as X-rays. He was wrong, but accidentally discovered radioactivity in the process. His experiment consisted of exposing his sample to the sunlight then placing it on photographic plates wrapped in black paper and later developing the plates. One day it was so overcast in Paris that he couldn't expose the compound to sunlight. He put his experiment aside, and in a few days developed the plates anyway. To his surprise they produced an image. The potassium uranyl sulfate was emitting some form of energy without having absorbed it from sunlight. He found that, unlike X-rays, the radiation could be bent by exposing it to a magnetic field.

Further experimentation, first by Becquerel and then by Marie and Pierre Curie, revealed that there are more radioactive materials and three types of radioactivity, but still no one knew exactly what form radioactivity took. This could only emerge after the structure of the atom had fallen under scrutiny.

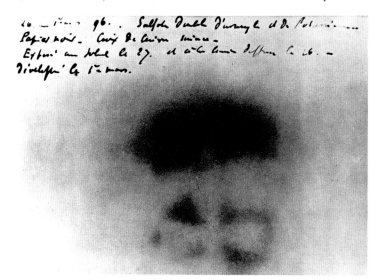

Becquerel's photographic plate revealing the radioactivity of uranium.

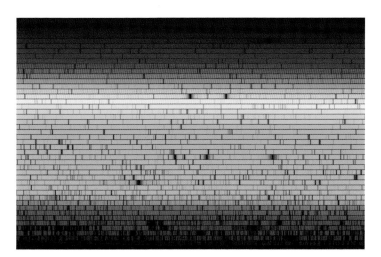

The black lines in the absorption spectrum of sunlight can be used to identify elements lying between the outer layers of the Sun and the observing instrument.

Hydrogen and helium

The 19th-century scientists had assumed that the Sun contained pretty much the same sort of stuff as the Earth. Without being able to visit the Sun to take samples, it was difficult to check. But one thing does come from the Sun all the time, and this would provide the answer: sunlight.

Lines in the light

When Isaac Newton first split sunlight into a spectrum of colours using a glass prism, he saw a continuous rainbow. In 1802, English chemist William Wollaston refined his method using a lens to focus the spectrum on to a screen, and found that there were black lines breaking it up. This is an absorption spectrum. The dark lines represent wavelengths of light that have been absorbed by something lying between the light source and the observer, though this was not known at the time. A few years later, in 1815, German physicist

and lens-maker Joseph von Fraunhofer used a diffraction grating in place of a glass prism and achieved a far more precise and detailed spectrum. He made systematic investigations of the solar spectrum and published his results. In the 1820s, William Talbot and John Herschel developed flame spectroscopy, showing that the spectrum of a flame produced by burning a metal was a kind of fingerprint which could identify the metal. Developments continued, with chemists noticing that the coloured bands in the absorption spectrum of an element precisely match the dark lines in its emission spectrum (the light produced when it is heated).

From the 1860s, the German team of Robert Bunsen and Gustav Kirchhoff systematically investigated the spectra of the chemical elements. As each element has its own spectral signature, it's possible to identify an element by matching a spectrum to a known sample.

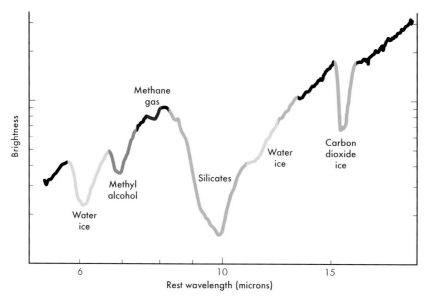

Today, spectra can reveal the composition even of objects which we can't see. This spectrum from a protostar forming 1,140 light years away shows water, carbon dioxide, methane, methyl alcohol and silicate rock. The protostar is hidden in dark clouds and can be examined only in infrared.

While studying a solar eclipse in 1868, French astronomer Pierre-Jules-César Janssen discovered a yellow line in the spectrum of the Sun which he could not identify. The English astronomer Norman Lockyer realized that as it didn't match any known element it must be a new one. He gave it the name 'helium' from the Greek word for sun, *helios*. (Helium was finally found on Earth in 1895.) Although his explanation was not widely accepted, it was the first evidence that the Sun is not made of the same stuff as Earth. Precisely the opposite was suggested by the work of another spectroscoper.

Parts and proportions

In 1863, English astronomer William Huggins was the first to apply spectroscopy to the stars. He noticed that there were many gaps in the spectra of starlight. These represented areas of the spectrum which were absorbed by elements in the atmosphere or surface of the star; some of the light produced within the star was not reaching Earth because of this absorption. The discovery that elements such as calcium and iron are present in stars was hugely significant: it suggested that the elements we have on Earth are present throughout the universe, that chemistry is literally universal. The assumption was, then, that the stars probably had much the same composition as the Earth, just as Kelvin had suggested. American astronomer Henry Norris Russell declared that if the Earth's crust was heated to the temperature of a star, it would produce much the same spectrum. But these conclusions were wrong.

READING THE STARS

The spectrum of a star can be read to show the atoms and ions present and can reveal the temperature and pressure at the surface. Light generated at the heart of the star travels (slowly) to the surface, where some of it is absorbed by atoms in the star's atmosphere. Each different ion absorbs light of a very precise frequency. From the frequency of light absorbed (the position of the dark bands in the absorption spectrum), it's possible to work out which ions are present in the atmosphere and in what concentrations.

Annie Jump Cannon, photographed here around 1900, was a pre-eminent astronomer at Harvard.

Star classification

In the early 20th century, under the direction of Annie Jump Cannon, astronomers at Harvard collected and analyzed the spectra of thousands of stars. Cannon had divided stars into seven classes based on differences in their spectra; the general assumption was that these reflected differences in the surface temperature of the stars, although there was no evidence to support that view. British astronomer Cecilia Payne

discovered the link with temperature using her knowledge of quantum physics (still a very new science) and the work on ionization energies of Indian physicist Meghnad Saha (1893–1956). Saha's equation relates the ionization state of an element to temperature and pressure. His work was refined by Ralph Fowler and Edward Milne in 1923 and 1924, making it easier to calculate the temperature of a star. The strength of an absorption line

CECILIA PAYNE (1900–79)

Cecilia Payne originally studied botany at Cambridge, but became increasingly interested in physics. After attending a lecture given by Arthur Eddington on general relativity, she turned her attention to astronomy. Arriving at Harvard in 1923, she worked on her doctoral thesis with Harlow Shapley, director of the observatory, and was assigned Henrietta Leavitt's desk.

After two years, Payne submitted her thesis. Her finding, that the composition of all stars is much the same and that they are mostly hydrogen and helium, didn't accord with current beliefs and Shapley and her external examiner, Henry Norris Russell, persuaded her not to make this claim. Instead of investigating her findings, she spent a lot of effort explaining why they must be wrong.

In 1929, using different methods, Russell came to the same conclusion as Payne. Her result was finally accepted and acknowledged as a brilliant piece of work. She continued to work at Harvard for the rest of her career. In 1934, she married Russian astrophysicist Sergei Gaposchkin, whom she met in Germany and helped to escape to the USA as a refugee. Thereafter they worked together on most of their projects. A lifelong chain smoker, Payne died from lung cancer in 1979.

'The fact that so many stars have identical spectra is in itself a fact suggesting uniformity of composition.'

Cecilia Payne, 1925

in a star's spectrum is directly related to the concentration of the corresponding element in the star's atmosphere. This means that the temperature and pressure of a star determine the extent to which the atoms in it are ionized.

Payne studied Cannon's stellar spectra and concluded that the different classes related to different surface temperatures, but not because the stars had differing compositions. She studied the spectral signatures of 18 different elements and found them present in all stars at similar proportions, regardless of the type of star. Most surprisingly, she found that all the stars, including the Sun, are composed primarily of hydrogen, and that hydrogen and helium together account for at least 98 per cent of the mass of a Sun-like star. This was considered a ridiculous idea.

As the work was Payne's PhD thesis, she couldn't afford for it to be dismissed. Her supervisor, Harlow Shapley, sent her conclusion to Russell, who denounced it as 'clearly impossible'. So in her thesis, submitted in 1925, Payne referred to the values she had found for the abundance of hydrogen and helium as 'almost certainly not real'.

But they were real, and within just a few years she was vindicated. Russell came to the same conclusion himself, by different methods, in 1929.

A hint of things to come

Even though Payne's findings about the abundance of hydrogen in stars weren't taken seriously until 1929, Arthur Eddington suggested as early as 1920 that stars might be powered by the nuclear fusion of hydrogen. He suggested that even if the stars contained only 5 per cent hydrogen, this would be sufficient to produce the energy observed coming from the Sun. At this point, too little was known about the structure of the atom for his idea to be developed into a full explanation.

'A star is drawing on some vast reservoir of energy by means unknown to us. This reservoir can scarcely be other than the sub-atomic energy which, it is known, exists abundantly in all matter; we sometimes dream that man will one day learn how to release it and use it for his service... [Francis] Aston has further shown conclusively that the mass of the helium atom is less than the sum of the masses of the 4 hydrogen atoms which enter into it... Now mass cannot be annihilated, and the deficit can only represent the mass of the electrical energy set free in the transmutation. We can therefore at once calculate the quantity of energy liberated when helium is made out of hydrogen. If 5 per cent of a star's mass consists initially of hydrogen atoms, which are gradually being combined to form more complex elements, the total heat liberated will more than suffice for our demands, and we need look no further for the source of a star's energy.'

Arthur Eddington, 1920

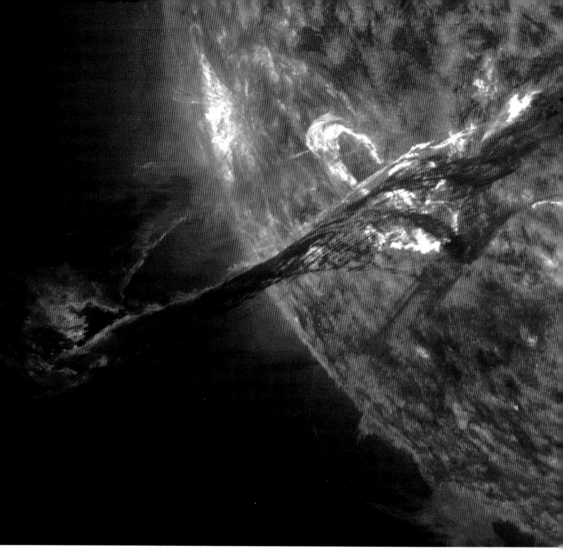

Deep within the Sun, hydrogen is fused into helium at the rate of 600–700 million tonnes a second. The photons released eventually emerge at the surface, producing the light, heat and other radiation of the Sun. The roiling turmoil of the interior is occasionally manifest in ejections of material, like this filament hurled out at 1,450 km (900 miles) per second.

Energy from proximity

Eight years later, in 1928, George Gamow calculated the conditions, under quantum theory, of two subatomic particles coming sufficiently close to each other to take part in a nuclear reaction. The particles would need to be close enough for the strong nuclear force which acts between protons and neutrons to overcome the electrostatic repulsion between them. In conventional physics this wouldn't happen, but quantum physics allows a mechanism called tunnelling by which it can occur. The Gamow factor was used in the subsequent decade to work out the rate at which nuclear reactions could be expected to take place, depending on the temperature and pressure within a star.

In 1939, in a ground-breaking paper called 'Energy Production in Stars', Hans Bethe proved that fusion produces the enormous energy emitted by stars. He set out two nuclear fusion paths for the production of energy from hydrogen in stars. Of these, the proton–proton chain (see box below) is the most relevant to Population III stars.

In the dense heart of stars, the process of nucleosynthesis continues, with helium itself a raw material for building larger atomic nuclei (see page 51). The Population III stars typically burned through their hydrogen quickly and ended their short lives in a dramatic supernova that blew them apart. The role of the Population III stars was fulfilled when they died, blasting out into space the metallic elements they had produced. These atoms became part of the interstellar medium and over time formed the material for new generations of stars of a type we can still see today, and even the one by which we live, the Sun.

NUCLEAR FUSION

There are several stages and more than one pathway to getting helium from hydrogen; it's not just a matter of squashing four hydrogen atoms together.

- Two protons fuse to form a diproton: a highly unstable form called helium-2.

- Just one in 10^{28} diprotons decays into deuterium, emitting a positron and a neutrino. This happens so quickly that the diproton stage is not observed (and not shown below): we'd either see the protons bouncing off one another or becoming deuterium.

- The deuterium combines with another proton, making helium-3 and losing a photon. That can then either fuse with a second helium-3 nucleus, making a helium-4 nucleus and two free protons, or fuse with a helium-4 nucleus, if there's one around, producing beryllium-7. This then decays to lithium-7, which fuses with another proton to make beryllium-8 and immediately decays into two helium-4 nuclei (normal helium nuclei).

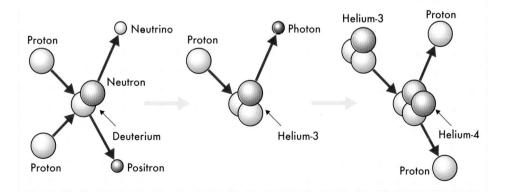

PUSHING AND PULLING IN A STAR

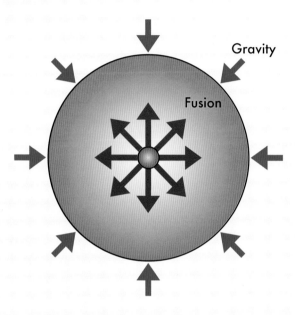

Gravity

Fusion

Once nuclear fusion starts, it exerts pressure pushing outwards from the core of the star. The photons moving through the star go in random directions, but as the centre is small the general trend of movement is outwards. Together the photons produce radiation pressure which counteracts gravity pulling the star inwards. When the two are balanced, the gravitational collapse stops and the star is in hydrostatic equilibrium (it stays the same size). This continues for most of the star's life.

Now you see it . . .

All this early star formation had another effect on the universe, and it is one which allows us to see those later stars, including our own. No one is exactly sure when things started to change, but at some point around 150 million years after the Big Bang, the clumping together of matter as the structure of the universe began to emerge produced significant temperature differences. Areas with higher density of energy and matter became hotter than the surrounding space. Eventually some of these areas of high energy density became stars, as we have seen. Energy poured from the hotter areas in the form of photons of various wavelengths, including high-energy ultraviolet radiation.

At this point the universe was still largely full of neutral atoms. The radiation was sufficiently powerful to strip the electrons from the hydrogen atoms – all the atom-building work that was done at recombination could be undone! The once-stable atoms of hydrogen were reduced once more to free protons and electrons, whizzing around in a charged plasma. But the universe had changed. It was a lot bigger than it had been before recombination, and this time the plasma was not dense enough to stop the free movement of photons.

The onslaught must have continued for a very long time, otherwise the electrons and protons would have quickly recombined. The effect would have begun as localized bubbles of ionized hydrogen close to the collapsing structures and early stars. The bubbles would have grown, as photons streamed through the areas of ionized gas to wreak havoc on the atomic gas just beyond. The bubbles expanded, overlapped and joined together. The pace would have picked up as more stars formed, pouring out more photons. After around 900 million years, the primordial gas was entirely ionized and light (and other electromagnetic radiation) could stream unimpeded in all directions. This period, known as reionization, brought the Dark Ages of the universe to an end. The universe was transparent again – and it remains so.

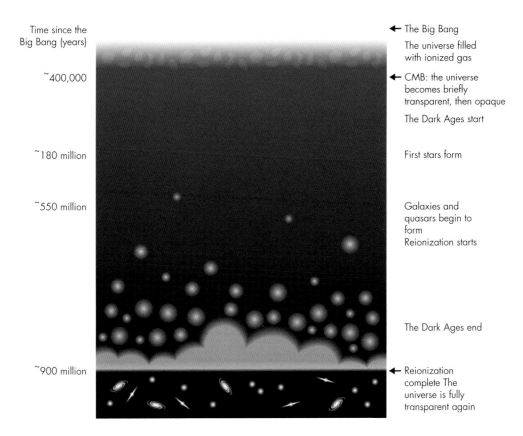

Time since the Big Bang (years)

← The Big Bang
The universe filled with ionized gas

~400,000 — ← CMB: the universe becomes briefly transparent, then opaque

The Dark Ages start

~180 million — First stars form

~550 million — Galaxies and quasars begin to form
Reionization starts

The Dark Ages end

~900 million — ← Reionization complete The universe is fully transparent again

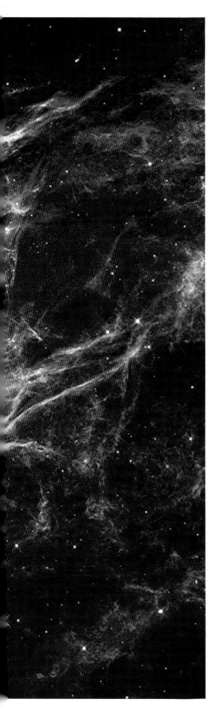

THE LIVES OF STARS

'The ways by which men arrive at knowledge of the celestial things are hardly less wonderful than the nature of these things themselves.'

Johannes Kepler (1571–1630)

A billion years after the Big Bang, the first stars had been and gone. Space was transparent and already held a delicate network of matter that poured light into the empty blackness. Within the giant filaments of matter, the next generation of stars was being born, making the universe we now see around us.

A tiny portion of the remnants of a supernova – all that is left of a giant star that died 8,000 years ago. Where the gas clouds from the exploding star meet colder, denser interstellar gas, the collision produces light. Many of the very first stars would have ended in the same way as this.

Part of a NASA animation of a hypernova, showing matter blasting away from the central star.

The end of the beginning

The giant Population III stars would have burned themselves out in millions of years, at the end of which they would probably have exploded in massive supernovae, scattering helium and other elements back into space, enriching the interstellar medium (ISM). As many of the first stars were larger and more energetic than most of today's stars, their final explosions are termed hypernovae – massive collapses that are even more dramatic than supernovae. Some extremely large stars might possibly have collapsed directly into black holes with no hypernova.

Where are they now?

Many of the objects we observe in the universe are no longer there: we 'see' them through the electromagnetic radiation they produced millions or billions of years ago. But after around 12–13 billion years we are unlikely to find many of the huge Population III stars.

There is possibly a relic of a single Population III hypernova. US cosmologists Volker Bromm and Avi Loeb believe a hypernova can sometimes produce a massive gamma-ray burst (GRB) so powerful that it may still be detected. The extinct star leaves behind a black hole. NASA's Swift satellite is searching for supernovae and hypernovae and has already found the GRB from one ancient hypernova, which could have been a Population III star. Bromm and Loeb predict that a tenth of the supernovae Swift will detect will date from the first billion years of the life of the universe. Most will probably be early Population II stars, but some could be Population III and may provide new and valuable information about the first stars.

Small survivors

Until the late 1990s, astronomers believed that all the earliest stars were giants so would no longer exist. Simulations in 2012 suggested that small stars could also form, probably in the aftermath of the supernova of a larger star. In 2018, astronomers using the Gemini Observatory based in Chile and Hawaii found a small ultra-metal-poor star

The yellow rectangle on the right of the image marks the location of the star 2MASS J18082002–5104378B, discovered in 2018. It is 13.5 billion years old and lies in the 'thin disk' area of the Milky Way.

within the Milky Way. It's a red dwarf with only 14 per cent of the mass of the Sun. It was reported to be 13.5 billion years old and still going strong – red dwarfs can last for trillions of years (see page 116).

The star 2MASS J18082002–5104378 B is the oldest in the galaxy. It's almost entirely composed of hydrogen and helium with only very tiny proportions of other elements and is the new record-holder for the lowest metallicity of any known star. It probably formed from the debris of one of the first generation of stars. The Sun, by contrast, is likely to be very many of generations from the first stars, having formed from material which had previously been through numerous short-lived stars.

The oldest star is just 2,000 light years from Earth in an active area of the Milky Way. It has a similar orbit around the galaxy's centre as the Sun, and its position suggests the disk of the Milky Way might be three billion years older than astronomers thought.

From death to life

Population II stars evolved in the first two billion years of star formation. More is known about these as there are plenty to observe and investigate. The clouds of gas that collapsed into stars were richer in helium than the primordial mix and contained heavier elements which had been produced in the Population III stars and at their demise.

Sun   Old record-holding star   Newly discovered star

A LATE STARTER?

In 2015, astronomers led by David Sobral of the University of Lisbon found what seems to be evidence of Population III stars in a galaxy reported to be 12.9 billion years old, called CR7 (or COSMOS Redshift 7). It's three times as bright as any other galaxy that old and contains a bright blue cloud consisting, apparently, of only hydrogen and helium. The rest of the galaxy has the signature of Population II stars. Even 12.9 billion years is young for a Population III star, so astronomers suspect that this may be an anomaly, forming from a cloud of primordial hydrogen and helium later than other Population III stars.

An artist's impression of the early CR7 galaxy. The blue stars are older, possibly Population III stars, while the redder ones are Population II stars.

When Population II stars ended in supernovae they released even more heavy elements into the interstellar medium. Population I stars began to form 10 billion years ago and are still forming. Typically, 1–4 per cent of a Population I star's mass is made up of elements heavier than hydrogen or helium. Population II stars have just a hundredth of this proportion, and Population III stars maybe just one ten-millionth.

As the process of star formation is still going on, we can observe it directly. Images from the Hubble Space Telescope have been crucial in unravelling the birth of stars.

Dust to dust...

The gas cloud of a stellar nursery can be 10^{14} km across, or 10,000 times the diameter of the solar system. The result of collapse means that there are several focuses of gravity, so the cloud breaks into clumps.

Photos taken with the Hubble Space Telescope show the vast, towering clouds of gas and dust, often dubbed 'star nurseries'. The so-called Pillars of Creation is the most famous example. The columns are light-years long.

Each clump will attract more gas from around itself, growing and increasing its gravity and attracting more gas.

At first, the cloud is not too dense, so energy emitted by the hot gas in the clump can escape as photons. As the clump keeps growing, it becomes too dense and dust-clogged for the photons to escape. Although the clumps of gas are glowing, we can't observe them with an optical telescope. The very brightest galaxy, discovered in 2015, is an early dusty galaxy of this type, observed around a billion years after the Big Bang. Although this small galaxy was sending out 10,000 times more energy than the Milky Way and burning with the light of 300 trillion suns, most of the energy that reaches us is in the infrared part of the spectrum. This is because only the longer wavelengths of radiation can penetrate the dust clouds.

The collapsing cloud is called a solar nebula. The rapid build-up of energy within the clump causes the temperature inside to soar and at this point it becomes a protostar.

The snappily-named galaxy WISE J224607.57-052635.0 was discovered with NASA's Wide-Field Infrared Survey Explorer (WISE). A black hole at the centre of the galaxy is responsible for the intensely bright radiation it pours out.

Multiple births

The Giant Molecular Clouds (GMCs) that give rise to stars now are unimaginably vast. The columns of the Pillars of Creation are only a small part of a much larger GMC. A GMC typically has many millions of times the mass of the Sun and can generate thousands of millions of stars.

As a GMC collapses, it breaks into fragments. Since it has more than one centre of gravitational focus, each formed around an area a bit denser than the average, it becomes increasingly 'lumpy'. Each collapsing fragment can form one or more protostars. A protostar is typically 10^{10} km across, with a temperature of 10,000 K. Each nascent protostar begins with only around 1 per cent of its final mass but draws in more matter, sweeping its local area free of gas and dust.

HOW BIG IS A STAR?

Studies of nearby star-forming clouds suggest that stars the size of the Sun and smaller are very common, but much larger stars are rare. Astrophysicists assumed that the same conditions probably exist elsewhere, with a fairly stable relationship between the mass of a star-forming cloud and the stars produced. But a 2018 study of a star-forming region 18,000 light years away, W43-MM1, found surprising results: very large stars, up to 100 times the size of the Sun, are common, but smaller stars are far less prevalent.

Peering into the nursery

Within our galaxy, the areas where stars are being created appear as nebulae. Nebulae look like fuzzy or cloudy patches of light, similar to a star that has been blurred. They include very different types of object: some are distant galaxies and others lie within the Milky Way. Some of those within the Milky Way are genuinely cloudy; they are the vast clouds of gas and dust from which stars are being created. The discovery that some nebulous areas are star nurseries followed 200 years of study of nebulae. Much of what we know about how they work follows from observations made using the Hubble Space Telescope.

The first person to study and catalogue nebulae was Charles Messier (see page 18). His favourite telescope produced magnification of x104 with a 19-cm (7.5-inch) lens. Today our best images of nebulae and the clouds where stars form are produced by telescopes sited in space. The Hubble Space Telescope, launched in 1990, gathered many such images over nearly 30 years using a primary mirror 2.4 m (8 ft) across. The next generation of space telescope, the James Webb, has a mirror 6.4 m (21 ft) across.

The Hubble Space Telescope orbits the Earth at an altitude of 569 km (353 miles), free from the distortion that the atmosphere produces. (Stars 'twinkle' when viewed from Earth because the atmosphere bounces the light around.) Some wavelengths of radiation are absorbed by the atmosphere and never reach ground level at all, including much ultraviolet, gamma-rays and X-rays (luckily for us, as they are damaging). Hubble works within the wavelength range of visible light and a little either side, in infrared and ultraviolet. It has several different instruments and cameras to record its observations, and data is sent back to Earth by radio link.

Data from Hubble has helped to narrow the age of the universe first to 13–14 billion years and, more recently, to 12–13 billion years. It has revealed how stars form, confirmed the existence of dark energy and identified quasars. A telescope in space was first proposed in 1923. American astrophysicist Lyman Spitzer suggested the development of the telescope in 1946.

Top: *A small part of a vast star-forming region of the Milky Way known as the Lagoon nebula. The nursery is 4,000 light-years away and 55 light-years across. It was first catalogued in 1654, and was imaged by the Hubble Space Telescope in 2018.* Beneath: *The Hubble Space Telescope above Earth.*

Hubble's image of the nebula NGC 346, taken in 2005, gives a clear picture of a star nursery. In the nebula, a gas cloud is collapsing to produce protostars and infant stars, some only half the size of the Sun.

Sibling rivalry

The protostars within a star nursery don't all grow at the same rate. Some are bigger and grow more quickly to the point where they are pouring out energy. A star grows by pulling in more gas from the cloud immediately around it, increasing its gravity and its ability to draw in more matter.

Some large, bright stars are of much greater mass than the Sun. They emit ultraviolet radiation at very high intensity, which heats the surrounding gas of the cloud. The heated gas glows, just like the gas inside a fluorescent light bulb. When the ultraviolet radiation reaches the edge of the active area of the cloud it drives the gas away, effectively boiling it off into the interstellar medium in a process called photoevaporation. Cut off from the supply of gas it was feeding on, the star can't grow any further. Some of the stars in the nursery will be frozen at a pre-star size, too small and too cold to begin nuclear fusion. The Hubble Space Telescope has revealed about 50 nearly-stars within the Eagle nebula caught in exactly this state.

Spare stuff for planets

As the temperature at the core of the protostar rises, increasing pressure slows gravitational collapse. The protostar continues to contract slowly and gravitational potential energy is

SEE FOR YOURSELF

On a dark, clear night it's possible to see evidence of the clouds of matter in the interstellar medium which lies between the star systems (as its name implies). Where matter is concentrated in great molecular clouds, it blocks light. If you find somewhere dark enough to see the Milky Way you will notice that it is not a uniformly bright band of stars but has darker areas with fewer stars. This is the effect produced by molecular clouds lying within a few thousand light years of Earth and obscuring the light from distant stars.

The Milky Way seen from Earth.

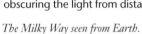

converted to heat. The core of the protostar radiates 1,000 times as much light as the Sun at this point.

Angular momentum is conserved as the cloud collapses. The cloud that was turning slowly speeds up as it contracts until it is spinning very rapidly. This is the same effect as a spinning ice-skater speeding up as she draws her arms close to her body.

At the same time, centripetal force acts against the inward pull of gravity. The effect is strongest around the equator of the new star and weakest at the poles. The result is that a flat band of matter, called a protoplanetary disk, forms on a plane around the equator. The material here could possibly be used to build planets and other objects. It also acts as an accretion disk, pulling in material from the surrounding gas cloud and feeding the growing star.

Out of the starting gate

A low-to-medium mass protostar becomes a T-Tauri star, a star of variable brightness. Its core temperature is still too low to start nuclear fusion, so for a few more millions of years the light it produces will come from the gravitational energy of its inward collapse. It can vary in brightness both randomly and periodically. Random brightness, changing over any interval from minutes to years, can be produced by irregularities in the accretion disk. The regular changes in brightness are probably produced by darker areas or sunspots on the surface which face Earth intermittently as the star rotates. The name 'T-Tauri star' comes from the first such star observed in the constellation Taurus, discovered in 1853 by English astronomer John Hind. T-Tauri itself is a very young star – around one million years old.

The young star continues to build from its accretion disk for a few million years until it reaches the critical mass and temperature at which fusion begins. Its mass then becomes fixed as it produces a strong solar wind, which prevents further accretion. Powered by nuclear fusion at its core, it has become a 'main sequence' star.

Another version

The English astronomer Norman Lockyer, who first discovered helium in the spectrum of the Sun, had an entirely different theory about the formation of stars. In a hypothesis based on the earlier ideas of von Mayer (see page 80), he suggested that stars are created from aggregated meteorites. Originally, he proposed, space was occupied by uniformly distributed meteorites. Through random movement and collisions, these grouped together to form swarms. The largest swarms are visible as nebulae. These condense as meteors are drawn closer together by gravity, eventually becoming so dense that they heat up and vaporize, forming stars. When stars eventually burn out and cool, they solidify into cold rock.

In this model, the final state of the universe will be 'heat death', with lumps of cold rock moving aimlessly forever. The bright bursts of supernovae, according to Lockyer, occur when star formation happens too quickly. Lockyer supported his theory

BROWN DWARFS

Not all stars make it to stardom. While protostars with enough mass (about 80 times the mass of the planet Jupiter) can make the transition to stars, those with less mass will never do so. Objects with 13 to 80 times the mass of Jupiter become brown dwarfs, dark objects that are hard to detect. Most brown dwarfs produce no visible light. They have too little mass to begin the nuclear fusion

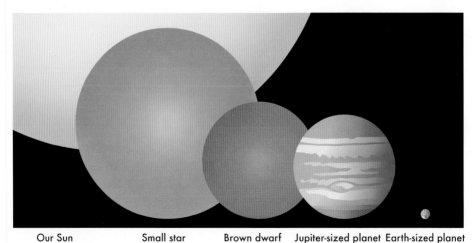

Our Sun   Small star   Brown dwarf   Jupiter-sized planet   Earth-sized planet

An artist's impression of a forming star drawing in matter from its accretion disk. In reality, the star would be much smaller compared to the disk.

of hydrogen, though a few manage other forms of activity. Those over 65 times the mass of Jupiter might convert lithium, and smaller ones might convert deuterium (^{2}H), into various isotopes. When they are visible, most are dark red or magenta, so look brownish. Even smaller than brown dwarfs are brown sub-dwarfs, and anything smaller than those is a gas giant planet.

Brown dwarfs can be as hot as stars when they first form, but without fusion to sustain them they cool and darken. Most of their radiation is at infrared wavelengths and astronomers study them with supercooled infrared cameras. Some older brown dwarfs are now about room temperature at the surface and have an atmosphere of methane and water vapour. The coolest one found so far, discovered in 2014, is as cold as the North Pole at -48 to -13 °C (-54 to -9 °F). It's just 7.2 light years from the Sun; its proximity and recent discovery underline how difficult these objects are to spot.

The existence of brown dwarfs was suggested by Indian astrophysicist Shiv Kumar in 1963; the name 'brown dwarf' was coined in 1975. No candidates were found until 1988, when a very faint companion to a star was discovered – but whether it should really be classed as a brown dwarf was unclear. The first undisputed brown dwarf emerged in 1994; a team of Spanish astrophysicists led by Rafael Rebolo found Teide 1 in the Pleiades cluster.

Although the number of brown dwarfs confirmed is only in the hundreds, an estimate published in 2017 suggests there are at least 25 billion and quite probably 100 billion in the Milky Way alone.

with evidence from spectroscopy, claiming that he found the spectra of supernovae (and comets and novae) to be very close to the spectral signature of meteorites, and citing the presence of a line close to one in the spectrum of magnesium.

English astronomers William and Margaret Huggins tested Lockyer's theory. They found that the line was near but not coincident with that of magnesium, and suggested that it signified a new element not known on Earth. This element became known as nebulium. The true nature of the nebular line was only uncovered in 1927 when American physicist and astrophysicist Ira Sprague Bowen (1898–1973) identified it as a sign of doubly ionized oxygen. This 'forbidden' form of oxygen cannot exist on Earth, but can occur in the extreme conditions of a supernova.

Grouping stars

The path a star takes from birth to death is difficult to determine as we can only observe a tiny portion of its life. This means we have to try to work out how stars move between

Norman Lockyer using Newall's telescope, the largest in the world in the early 1870s.

WHICH CAME FIRST, STARS OR GALAXIES?

Stars are concentrated in galaxies, and galaxies exist in clusters and even superclusters. In between are areas of largely empty space (so far as we can tell). But the formation of galaxies remains largely a mystery.

Astronomers suspect that the Population III stars formed before galaxies. As more and more stars formed, groups that we can call galaxies emerged about a billion years after the Big Bang. An alternative is that regions lumpy with matter drew together to make galaxies. Smaller star-dense regions combined into large areas, eventually making galaxies. Galaxies still combine and collide, so this process is ongoing.

the states we can see, and the various paths they might take. The first step was to group stars by similarities.

From earliest times, people have observed that some stars are brighter than others. The first person to try to catalogue stars according to their brightness was Ancient Greek astronomer Hipparchus of Nicaea. In the 2nd century BC he compiled a catalogue of at least 850 stars visible to the naked eye (in the pre-light-pollution night sky). His catalogue has not survived, but it formed the basis of the later catalogue produced by Ptolemy. Hipparchus divided stars into three classes according to their brightness – effectively, bright, medium and dim.

The Graeco-Roman Egyptian Claudius Ptolemy (*c.* AD 100–170) was the most influential ancient astronomer; his model of an Earth-centred solar system prevailed for 1,500 years. Ptolemy's *Almagest* is the most complete surviving ancient astronomical text. It contains tables to help calculate the positions of the planets in the past, present and future, and a star catalogue based on the work of Hipparchus. The catalogue lists 48 constellations visible in the sky from his location in Alexandria, Egypt. Ptolemy

extended the catalogue, giving numerical values for the brightness (magnitude) of the stars on a scale of 1 to 6. The brightest stars are rated 1 and the dimmest 6. This scale of measurement for apparent magnitude is still used, though in modified form. Maps showing stars at different sizes actually represent their apparent magnitude.

In Raphael's fresco The School of Athens, *Ptolemy (in the yellow robe, on the right) is shown holding a globe.*

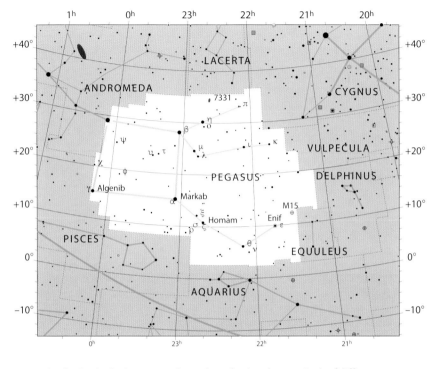

A star chart showing the magnitude of different stars.

The modern scale extends beyond 1 into negative numbers, with the Sun having magnitude -26.74. It goes well above 6 for objects that are visible with a telescope but not with the naked eye. Objects no longer need to be a whole number on the scale. Today a star is considered 1st magnitude if its brightness falls between 0.5 and 1.50.

In the 19th century, English astronomer Norman Pogson established a mathematical scale based on the premise that a star of magnitude 1 is considered 100 times brighter than a star of magnitude 6. As there are five steps between the ends of the scale, the multiple for each step is $100^{1/5}$ or a factor of about 2.51. This means a magnitude-1 star is 2.51 times brighter than a magnitude-2 star, and 2.51 x 2.51

times brighter than a magnitude-3 star, and so on. Pogson fixed the standard for his scale as Polaris (magnitude 2). The scale is clearly extendible in either direction, enabling astronomers to give the magnitude of bodies brighter than a magnitude-1 star and dimmer than a magnitude-6 star.

Later astronomers, discovering Polaris to be slightly variable, changed the reference star to Vega (magnitude 0). The advent of photosensors in the 1950s made it possible to measure the intensity of light from a star with great accuracy.

Seeming and being

The apparent magnitude of stars seen from Earth tells us relatively little. Two stars that look the same size could be very different:

one might be nearby and small, the other far distant but much larger. When we see stars in the night sky, they appear as though on the inside of a dark dome – there is nothing to give a sense of depth, to show that some are much further away than others.

Early astronomers weren't able to judge the absolute magnitude, or luminosity, of stars. Today we can work out a star's absolute magnitude based on its luminosity viewed from a standard distance of 10 parsecs (32.6 light years). For example, the Sun is very close to us and has an apparent magnitude of -26.74. The large star Betelgeuse in the constellation Orion has an apparent magnitude 0.42. Its radius is 1,400 times that of the Sun, but it's 600 light years away. If we compare the magnitude of both at a distance of 10 parsecs, Betelgeuse is far brighter than the Sun – in fact, it's 18,700 times as bright.

While being able to quantify their brightness is useful, it doesn't tell us much about the stars. One star could be more luminous than another because it is hotter or larger. It doesn't tell us whether stars are more luminous early or late in their lives, or whether their luminosity changes at all. Such information is vital to understanding the lives of stars and the story of the universe. To work this out, astronomers needed more information about the composition and temperature of stars. That began to become available with the invention of spectroscopy in the 19th century. As we have seen (see page 84), spectroscopy revealed the presence of helium in the Sun before this element was discovered on Earth. It became an increasingly important way of investigating the stars.

The first scheme of classification by spectra was introduced by Italian astronomer Angelo Secchi in the 1860s and 1870s. He first identified three classes:

- I   White and blue stars with heavy hydrogen lines in their spectra

- II   Yellow stars with less prominent hydrogen lines and some lines for heavier elements

- III   Orange to red stars, with complex-spectra.

He later added two more classes:

- IV   Stars with a strong carbon presence in their spectra (added in 1868)

- V   Stars with unusual characteristics flagged by bright emissions in their spectra (added in 1877)

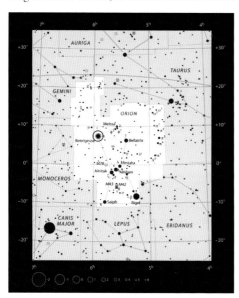

The location of Betelgeuse in Orion (circled in red).

The Draper catalogue

In the 1880s an ambitious star-cataloguing venture was completed at Harvard Observatory. It was the legacy of Henry Draper, a physician and amateur photographer. Draper took the first photograph of the spectrum of a star (Vega) in 1872. He pushed forwards developments in the design of equipment and in techniques, but died of pleurisy at the age of 45 in 1882. His widow established a fund to produce a full catalogue of stellar spectra in his honour. American astronomer Edward Pickering took charge of the project, employing a large team of women to process the spectra. Their work became the Draper catalogue. The method for producing the spectra for the catalogue was similar to that used by Secchi (and previously Fraunhofer), but the results were preserved as a photograph. Light from each star was split by a glass prism into its spectrum and then focused on a photographic plate, which recorded

it. The female astronomers, known as 'Pickering's Computers' or even 'Pickering's Harem', were woefully underpaid, at a few cents an hour. Yet over a period of years they produced a work of ground-breaking importance on which the astronomy of the 20th century was founded. By the end of the project the team had processed nearly a quarter of a million stars.

The first volume of the catalogue was published in 1890 and gave the spectral classifications of 10,000 stars. The classification method for this volume was designed by Williamina (or Wilhelmina) Fleming and based on Secchi's scheme, which used the dark lines in the absorption spectra. No one knew the full meaning of the dark lines at this point, but this didn't limit their usefulness in 'fingerprinting' the stars.

The Harvard College Observatory astronomers in 1917.

E. Woods | Evelyn F. Leland | Florence Cushman | Grace Brooks | Mary H. Vann | Henrietta Leavitt | Mollie O'Reilly

BETWEEN THE LINES

The relation of the dark lines in absorption spectra to the movement of electrons between energy levels in an atom would not be revealed until the work of Niels Bohr. The electrons can exist only at specific energy levels, or orbitals, within an atom. If the atom is in a stable state, the electrons pootle around in their orbitals without change. If an atom is supplied with exactly the right amount of energy in the form of a photon, an electron can be boosted from one energy level to the next. Each electron orbital is associated with a particular level of energy, and electrons can only make a jump if they gain just the right amount of extra energy.

Imagine that a cloud of hydrogen gas lies between a source of light and an observer recording its spectrum. The light source produces photons of lots of different amounts of energy. Any photons with exactly 10.2 eV (electron volts) will be snapped up by hydrogen atoms which can use these photons to boost their electron from the first energy level to the second. They can also grab photons with 1.89 eV to boost the electron from the second to the third energy level. The observer will see black lines corresponding to these values in the spectrum of light that has passed through the hydrogen cloud, because photons with these energies have been removed. There are equivalent values for boosting electrons between energy levels in the atoms of other elements. So, by looking at absorption spectra, a skilled spectroscoper can work out which elements are present in a cloud of gas. When we look at the Sun or another star, the source of light is the core of the star and the star's atmosphere provides the cloud of gas that is grabbing some of the photons.

Alta Carpenter | Annie J. Cannon | Dorothy Block | Arville D. Walker | Frank Hinkley | Edward S. K...

WILLIAMINA FLEMING (1857–1911)

Fleming was born Williamina Stevens in Dundee, Scotland. She attended a local school until the age of 14, then became a pupil-teacher there. She married at the age of 20 and emigrated to Boston, USA, with her husband. He left her when she was pregnant, and she took a job as Pickering's maid to support herself and her infant son. In 1881, Pickering employed her to carry out clerical work at Harvard Observatory. When Pickering was given the task of producing the Draper catalogue in 1886, her circumstances improved. Soon she was in charge of a team of women processing the spectral photographs of stars. Fleming worked out a classification scheme based on that of Secchi, but improved on it greatly – it still underlies the schemes used today. She was appointed Curator of Astronomical Photographs at Harvard in 1899.

Over a period of four years Fleming and her team processed the spectra of tens of thousands of stars. She discovered the Horsehead nebula and another 58 nebulae, 310 variable stars and ten supernovae. She also discovered white dwarfs, very hot dense stars at the end of their lives, publishing on them in 1910. In recognition of her achievements, she was made an honorary member of the Royal Astronomical Society of London in 1906. She died of pneumonia in 1911 at the age of 54.

Letters and numbers

Starting with Secchi's scheme, Fleming used Roman numerals up to five, but created more categories and assigned them letters of the alphabet instead. She started with A to N, and later added O, P and Q (O for stars with spectra consisting mostly of bright lines, P for planetary nebulae, and Q for stars that didn't fit into any other class). Another woman at the Harvard Observatory,

Antonia Maury (Draper's niece), developed her own stellar classification system which returned to Roman numerals, running from I to XXII. It put her at odds with Pickering and she left Harvard for some years, but her system fed into later work.

Another of the 'computers', Annie Jump Cannon, modified the system Fleming had developed, dropping half the categories and re-ordering the others to give the

The Horsehead nebula, in the constellation of Orion, is 1,500 light years from Earth. Williamina Fleming discovered it in 1888.

sequence O, B, A, F, G, K, and M, and P and Q for the planetary nebulae and oddities. The reason for the reordering was to sequence by temperature rather than the amount of hydrogen, so making a physical property of the stars the determining factor. In Cannon's sequence, O represents the hottest category of stars and M the coolest; the Sun is a G-category star. This switch relied on working out what the temperature of the star must be from the spectrum of energy emitted.

The effective temperature of a star, deduced from its spectrum, is the temperature an ideal black body (see page 112) with the same surface area would need in order to produce the same energy output. Cannon continued to refine her work, developing a system for classifying stars intermediate between two categories. By 1912 she had established the basis of the current system and it was adopted by the International Astronomical Union in 1922. It was, unfairly, called the Harvard system rather than the Cannon system. Cannon catalogued more than 350,000 stars in the course of her career and by the time she had perfected her skills could assess and classify a star in just three seconds.

Pickering's team of 'computers' at work at the Harvard Observatory.

LIGHT, HEAT AND BLACK BODIES

If you heat an object sufficiently it will begin to glow, radiating light. At first the light is red, but it becomes yellow and, eventually, white as the temperature rises. In 1900, Max Planck realized that the wavelength of light emitted by a heated object relates directly to its temperature. As temperature rises, the wavelength of the radiation given off becomes shorter and the intensity of the radiation increases.

In physics, an 'ideal black body' is one which absorbs all the radiation falling onto it, reflecting none – so it looks black. There is no object known that is a perfect black body, but a lump of charcoal comes close. The ideal black body is the standard for establishing the link between temperature and wavelength. Astronomers can work out the temperature of a star by comparing its spectrum with standardized spectra for black bodies at different temperatures. From this it is possible to work out the intensity of the star's light.

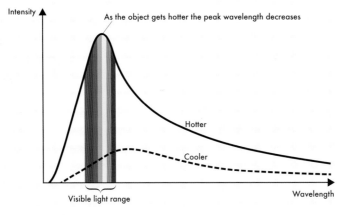

The spectrum of the Sun matches the spectrum of radiation emitted by a black body heated to 5,777K. This is considered to be the temperature at the Sun's surface.

Infrared goggles and cameras work by picking up the high wavelength infrared radiation given off by living bodies. Body temperature is fairly low, so we can't see a person or animal in the dark (when they are not reflecting visible light) but they do glow in infrared all the time because of their body warmth (see the image on the facing page).

Putting the parts together

The Harvard system now subdivides each of Cannon's classes into ten sub-groups depending on absorption features of the spectrum. This gives a good indication of the temperature of a star, but doesn't say anything about its luminosity. It's impossible to tell the type or brightness of a star just from its Harvard class (O, B, A, F, G, K, M). In 1943, William Wilson Morgan and Philip C. Keenan added an extra layer of classification, producing the Morgan–Keenan (or MK) stellar classification system used today.

An infrared image clearly shows the warmth of living things in this waterside scene.

The Morgan–Keenan system starts with the Harvard letter, then adds a number in the range 0–9 (0 = hottest, 9 = coolest) to show where in that temperature band a star lies. It uses a Roman numeral to indicate luminosity, from 0 (or Ia) to V, with V the dimmest. Luminosity is determined by the width of certain absorption lines in the spectrum, which vary with the density of the star's atmosphere. As a result, this system can distinguish between stars of different types, such as red dwarf or supergiant (see page 114), because they are of different density. Using the MK classification, the Sun is a G2V star: a standard, yellow, main-sequence star.

STAR CLASSIFICATION

Stars categorized by temperature:

O more than 30,000 K, described as blue

B 10,000–30,000 K, blue-white

A 7,500–10,000 K, white

F 6,000–7,500 K, yellow-white

G 5,200–6,000 K, yellow

K 3,700–5,200 K, orange

M 2,400–3,700 K, red

Stars categorized by luminosity:

0 (Ia+) hypergiants or extremely luminous supergiants

Ia luminous supergiants

Iab intermediate luminous supergiants

Ib less luminous supergiants

II bright giants

III normal giant stars

IV subgiants

V main-sequence (dwarf) stars

Class O   Class B   Class A   Class F   Class G   Class K   Class M

Part of Antonia Maury's work involved dividing stars according to the width of their spectral lines. Danish astronomer and chemist Ejnar Hertzsprung realized that stars with narrow lines tended to move less against the background stars than others with the same spectral classification. He believed this indicated that the narrow-line stars were more luminous. He used parallax to work out the distances to several groups of such stars, which allowed him to estimate their absolute magnitude.

In 1913, Henry Norris Russell studied giant stars identified by Hertzsprung from Maury's data, nearby stars with known parallax, and several clusters and groups for which distances and absolute magnitudes could be calculated. He plotted spectral class against absolute magnitude.

Hertzsprung and Russell discovered a pattern that put stars into groups; this became known as the Hertzsprung–Russell diagram. Modern versions plot temperature against luminosity (the theoretical version, as it uses calculated values), or colour against absolute magnitude (the observational version, as it uses values that can be measured directly). Both sets of axes effectively show the same thing, as colour corresponds with temperature and luminosity relates directly to absolute magnitude.

The Hertzsprung–Russell diagram is now one of the most useful tools in astronomy. An astronomer can work out what type of star he or she is observing just by finding its place on the graph. For example, if a star is found to be hot (so on the left-hand side of the diagram), it will fall into one of three groups: a white dwarf, a main-sequence star, or a hyper/super giant. If it has low luminosity (or absolute magnitude), it must be a white dwarf. If it has very high luminosity or

---

RADIATION AND SIZE

The relationship between the size of a star and the radiation it emits is defined by the Stefan–Boltzmann law, deduced by Josef Stefan in 1879 from experimental data and derived theoretically by Ludwig Boltzmann in 1884. It states that the total energy (all wavelengths) radiated per unit surface area of a black body in a fixed time is directly proportional to the temperature to the power of 4 (that is, temperature x temperature x temperature x temperature). Consequently, if we know the surface area of a star or other body and can measure the radiation emitted, we can work out its temperature. If we know the temperature and one other value, we can work out the final value, either the energy it releases or its surface area.

---

absolute magnitude, it must be a hyper/super giant. And if it has high, but not extremely high, luminosity or absolute magnitude, it's a main-sequence star.

The next obvious question is – what does it all mean?

Curating the astronomical zoo

By the middle of the 20th century, astronomers had a good means of classifying stars; they also had optical telescopes and radio telescopes. They knew stars fall into clear groups, as shown by the Hertzsprung–Russell diagram, but not how these relate to star evolution.

The main sequence

A survey of the night sky reveals stars at different stages of their lives but also at different times in history, because of their distance from us. So while we see nearby stars pretty much as they are now, we see very distant stars as they were thousands or, in distant galaxies, millions or even billions of years ago.

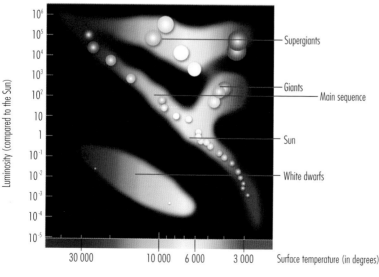

The Hertzsprung–Russell diagram that plots the temperature and luminosity of stars, showing the main groups into which they fall. The long, diagonal grouping shows main sequence stars – those in the active part of their life.

Most stars in the universe are on the main sequence. They have gone through the stages of protostar and T-Tauri star and are now in their mid-life, forging helium from hydrogen at their core. This makes sense statistically, as stars spend a relatively short time getting going at the start and winding down at the end of their lives. As the Hertzsprung–Russell diagram shows, main sequence stars can be of any size from O to M; their life cycle varies according to their size.

Slow and steady

The smallest a star can be to begin fusion is about 0.075 times the mass of the Sun (solar masses). These stars are classed as red dwarfs; they are cool and last a long time, probably trillions of years. Their size is

0.075 to 0.5 solar masses. In those that are 0.4 to 0.5 solar masses, fusion takes place throughout the star, not just in the core, which greatly extends the time they can continue to form helium. Red dwarfs have only around 10 per cent of the luminosity of the Sun, so although most stars in the Milky Way are red dwarfs, none can be seen with the naked eye. Because red dwarfs live for such a long time, the universe is not old enough to hold any but young red dwarfs. Astronomers can only theorize about how their lives might end. The red dwarf is likely to go straight to white dwarf phase (see facing page) without forming a nebula; it doesn't have enough gravitational energy to fuse helium into heavier elements.

Stars like our Sun are yellow dwarfs. Typically from 0.8 to 1.4 times the mass of

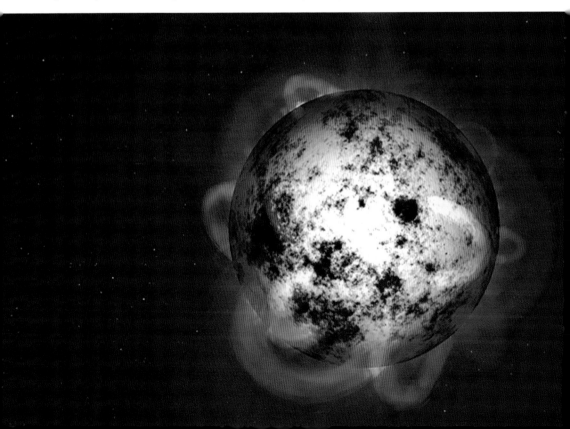

WHAT'S THE DIFFERENCE?

There is no clear dividing line between red dwarf and yellow dwarf stars. Astronomers have come to categorize them according to their size, temperature and the wavelength of radiation they produce, but there is in fact a continuum of stars from cooler to warmer, from smaller to larger. They did not form by radically different methods or come from radically different places. Other civilizations, from other worlds, might come up with completely different divisions between these stars.

the Sun, they are main-sequence stars that will last billions of years. The Sun has an expected total lifespan of about 10 billion years. White stars are hot main-sequence stars larger than the Sun, with mass 1.4–2.1 times that of the Sun.

Fast and furious

The next level of star, between 10 and 100 times the mass of the Sun, is a blue giant. It has 10–1,000 times the luminosity of the Sun. Like the Population III stars it superficially resembles, a blue giant is very hot and active and consequently short-lived. Blue supergiants and hypergiants are even bigger and brighter. The brightest ever found is 10 million times as bright as the Sun. Blue giants, supergiants and hypergiants are main-sequence stars.

Inset: *Eta Carinae is a two-star system that is four million times brighter than the Sun. The main star is a luminous blue variable star, probably only around one million years old and likely to end with a supernova relatively soon.*

Main: *An artist's impression of a red dwarf with an orbiting exoplanet (lower right). The arcing prominences are a result of magnetic activity.*

How stars eat themselves

What stars do during their time on the main sequence is to consume the materials they are made of. As we have seen (page 89), at the heart of stars, hydrogen is fused into helium. Four hydrogen nuclei form a single helium nucleus, but the helium nucleus has slightly less mass than the hydrogen nuclei added together. The extra mass is emitted as energy (photons). This follows Einstein's equation:

$$E = mc^2$$

where E is the energy produced, m is the difference in mass between the starting and finishing particles and c^2 is the speed of light squared. The difference in mass between the hydrogen nuclei and the helium nucleus is tiny, 4.8×10^{-29} kg (that's 0.[28 zeroes]48 kg), but the speed of light squared is a huge number. The result is that the energy produced from each tiny act of atomic fusion is about four trillionths of a joule (4.3×10^{-12} joules). That doesn't sound much, but in the heart of a star lots of hydrogen is being fused every second. In a star like the Sun, there is enough hydrogen to keep fusion going for around 10 billion years.

Ramping up production

If a star is large enough and hot enough, it can switch to a different mode called CNO (carbon-nitrogen-oxygen) nucleosynthesis. It can only do this if the temperature reaches 20 million K.

CNO nucleosynthesis is more productive than the proton–proton chain, and is the dominant path for producing helium in stars more than 1.3 times the mass of the Sun. The cycle was proposed independently by Carl von Weizsäcker in 1938 and Hans Bethe in 1939. It can only take place in the presence of carbon, which catalyzes the reaction in the sequence:

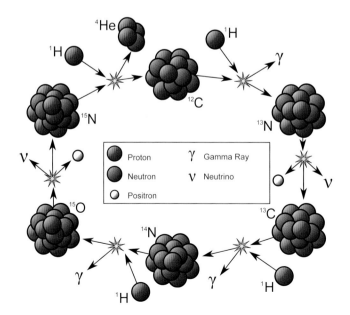

The CNO cycle produces helium in the presence of a carbon catalyst in stars larger than the Sun.

- a carbon-12 nucleus captures a proton and emits a gamma ray, producing nitrogen-13

- nitrogen-13 is unstable; it decays to carbon-13, emitting a positron (a beta particle)

- carbon-13 captures a proton and becomes nitrogen-14, emitting a gamma-ray

- the nitrogen-14 captures another proton and becomes oxygen-15, emitting a gamma-ray

- oxygen-15 becomes nitrogen-15, emitting a positron

- nitrogen-15 captures a proton and produces a helium nucleus (alpha particle) and carbon-12, so returning the original catalyst.

This only works if there is some carbon to start with, so it wasn't an option for the first stars but makes for efficient fusion in Population II and I stars.

Most carbon is fused inside red giant stars. The atmosphere of a red giant is cool enough for the gaseous carbon to condense as solid particles, that is, groups of atoms which stick together. Radiation pressure from within the star forces the particles out into space and they become ingredients of the interstellar medium. The same process carries other condensed elements into the interstellar medium. Even before a star has died, it is adding to the cosmic mix.

THE PHOTON'S LONG JOURNEY

Star matter is very dense, about 150 times the density of water. As each reaction takes place within the star, the surplus energy is released as a gamma-ray photon. The photon bumps into an atom and is re-radiated, often heading in a different direction. Far from travelling consistently at the speed of light, it travels at speed for a tiny distance before hitting another atom and having to stop and be redirected. Its average speed is about a quarter of a millimetre per second, or less than 2 cm per minute.

Sooner or later (usually later) each photon accidentally finds its way to the radiative zone, a huge area that occupies nearly half the depth of the star. Typically it will take a photon many thousands of years to make this journey. In the radiative zone, photons continue to be reradiated, but now their wavelength increases. They are downgraded to visible light and other longer-wavelength forms of energy. The last 30 per cent of the depth of the star is a convective zone. From here, the energy is carried by convection currents, as hot gas loops round in a circle from the depths to the surface.

From the surface of the star, the energy can escape into space. The photons, now with different levels of energy, stream forth from the star, making up the mix of visible light, infrared, ultraviolet, X-rays and other forms of radiation we can detect. The journey to the surface could have taken 100,000 years. A photon then covers the distance from the Sun to the Earth in just eight minutes.

The star cluster NGC 3532 contains around 400 stars. Some of the smaller ones are still blue; many larger ones have already become red giants and even larger ones have already ended their lives in supernovae. The cluster is 1,300 light years from Earth and around 300 million years old.

Ageing stars

For stars, ageing comes sooner the larger they are. As large stars of 0.5 to 8–10 times the mass of the Sun age, they become red giants or supergiants.

When such a star has fused all the hydrogen at its core into helium, and nuclear reactions cease, the core contracts under its own gravity. There is no longer any outward pressure from fusion to balance the inward pull of gravity, so the equilibrium is lost and gravity predominates. But the contraction pulls more hydrogen from further out in the star into an area where the temperature and pressure are high enough for fusion. Hydrogen fusion then begins in a shell around the core. The result is that the outer areas of the star expand massively. The energy of the fusing hydrogen in the shell is spread over a larger area, so the average temperature falls. As the star cools, the visible light that is radiated shifts towards the red end of the spectrum – it becomes a red giant.

What happens next depends on the size of the star. In a star of 0.5 to 2 solar masses, the core will become increasingly dense and hot until it can fuse helium, forming the heavier elements carbon and oxygen. When it reaches the critical conditions, at about 100 million K, the entire core begins to fuse helium simultaneously in a so-called 'helium flash'. Larger stars start helium fusion more gradually, without the flash. When, in turn, the helium of the core is exhausted, the core shrinks again. Helium can begin fusing in a shell outside the core, just as the hydrogen did. Hydrogen can also fuse in further shells, beyond the helium shell.

After around a billion years as a red giant, the star, massively expanded, ejects its outer layers to form a cloud-like planetary nebula leaving in the centre just the dense carbon-oxygen core, called a white dwarf. A white dwarf is typically about the size of Earth but with 200,000 times the density of Earth. If we could bring a single teaspoon of the material of a white dwarf to Earth, it would weigh 15 tons. This is the fate that eventually awaits the Sun.

White dwarfs are still hot and still radiate energy, but they will slowly cool. One day they won't produce enough energy to glow and they will become black dwarfs: cold, incredibly dense lumps of matter that are invisible in the universe. There cannot be any black dwarfs yet as it will take trillions of years for white dwarfs to cool to this extent.

The smudgy red circle bottom centre is a helium flash – a white dwarf caught in the act of expanding back to red dwarf size to continue fusing helium.

Going, going, gone

Larger stars die in different ways. Stars at least ten times the mass of the Sun can go beyond carbon-oxygen to fuse even heavier elements up to iron and nickel. Iron is the heaviest element that can be formed in the heart of a star. Fusing elements up to iron and nickel releases energy, but it requires an input of energy to make heavier elements so they can't be made by stellar nucleosynthesis. Finally, when stars are unable to fuse the iron, they die catastrophically.

BURNING THROUGH THE LAYERS

Large stars that fuse heavier elements don't last as long as smaller ones. A star like the Sun can burn hydrogen for around 10 billion years. A star with 25 times the mass of the Sun can fuse carbon, but only for about 600 years; then it can fuse neon for a year, and oxygen for six months. When it reaches a temperature of 3 billion K it can fuse silicon into iron, but exhausts its supply in a single day, leaving only an iron core.

An artist's impression of a gamma ray burst, the brightest and most powerful phenomenon in the universe. Created when a massive star explodes, a gamma ray burst usually lasts just seconds or hours.

This composite image of an area of the Small Magellanic Cloud includes the first neutron star found outside our galaxy. Its location is the blue spot inside the red circle on the left.

When the core is iron, no more nuclear fusion is possible. The sudden halt to energy production makes the core contract and the outer layers fall in on it. But they collapse inwards so rapidly that they bounce off the iron core at a speed close to the speed of light. A shockwave blasts the star apart in an explosion that briefly glows 100 million times more brightly than the original star – sometimes as brightly as an entire galaxy.

As the core collapses inwards, the pressure at its heart is so intense that atoms are crushed – protons and electrons are forced together to become neutrons.

The core of the ex-star consists entirely of neutrons: it becomes a neutron star. The matter of a neutron star is so dense that a teaspoonful of it would weigh 4 billion tons. The core of the star still has more than the mass of the Sun, but it is crammed into a blob just 16 km (10 miles) across.

Enormous stars, with mass 30 times that of the Sun, don't even leave a neutron star behind. They, too, end with a supernova, but the material at the core is under such immense gravity that it becomes a black hole. The star is gone; but in its end are new beginnings.

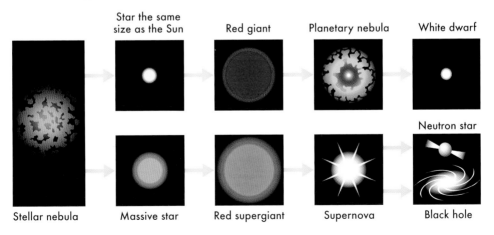

The lives of stars, big and small.

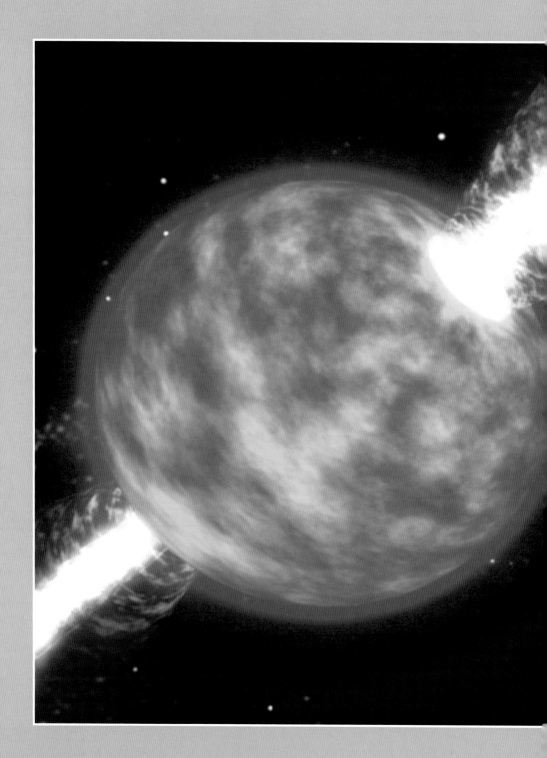

CHAPTER 6

THE 'PHOENIX OF NATURE'

*'These burning suns . . . together with the
retinue of their planets dissolved by the ineffable
heat, will disperse the material of their masses
in the old space of their sphere of formation
and there the materials for new formations are
provided through the same mechanical laws,
through which again the empty space can be
populated with worlds and systems . . . this
phoenix of nature, which burns itself only to rise
rejuvenated from its ashes to new life through all
infinity of time and space.'*

Immanuel Kant, 1755

We have no evidence of the first
hypernovae which destroyed the
Population III stars. They must have
been spectacular beyond imagining.
What astronomers have learned of
supernovae has come from those we can
witness, the demise of Population I stars
in the Milky Way and other galaxies.

*This artist's impression shows the moments before a large Wolf–Rayet
star goes supernova, when jets of matter are ejected at close to the
speed of light.*

Seeing supernovae

Supernovae burn so brightly that a few are visible from Earth even with the naked eye. The last to have been readily visible was Kepler's supernova of 1604.

Guests in the sky

On 4 July 1054, Chinese and Arab astronomers recorded a particularly bright supernova, or 'guest star'. Archaeological evidence suggests that it was also observed by indigenous North Americans. Chinese astronomers have the longest tradition of continuous star-gazing and reporting, and the records left by these early naked-eye astronomers have proved invaluable.

Chinese records mention 75 'guest stars' in the years between 532 BC and 1054, although these may not all have been supernovae. Since 1054, only two have been visible to the naked eye. Of the recorded 'guest stars', the earliest to be identified as a probable supernova was in AD 185. According to the Chinese text, it remained visible for either eight or 20

months (depending on interpretation). The supernova remnant G315.4-2.3 is now found in the region of sky where the guest star was reported. Chinese astronomers recorded another guest star in AD 393, now linked with the supernova remnant SN393 in the constellation of Scorpius (although its identification is not certain). Other possible supernova events occurred in AD 369, 386, 437, 827 and 902 – which seems a lot for just over 500 years – but no remnants have been associated with them.

The next spectacular supernova event definitely witnessed was in 1006. This was apparently the brightest star ever to have been seen in the night sky. It was recorded in China, Egypt, Iraq, Italy, Japan and Switzerland, and possibly France, Syria and North America. In 2003 a team led by American astronomer Frank Winkler associated the account with a supernova remnant that is now almost invisible. By watching the speed at which the remnant grows, they calculated that it was about 7,100 light years away from Earth (so the

This petroglyph left by the Anasazi people at Penasco Blanco in New Mexico might record the supernova of 1054. At intervals of 18.5 years, the Moon and Earth are in the same positions relative to the stars as they were in 1054. When the Moon is in the position indicated by the hand in the sky above Penasco Blanco, a telescope reveals the remnant of SN1054 at the position of the star in the petroglyph.

> *'A guest star appeared within Nan-men; it was as big as half a mat; it was multicoloured and it fluctuated. It gradually became smaller and disappeared in the sixth month of the year following the next year. According to the standard prognostication this means insurrection.'*
>
> Fan Yeh, *Book of Han*, c.450

event witnessed in 1006 actually happened around 6106 BC). It was probably a type-1a supernova and these always have the same luminosity. Calculating from its distance, we can tell that its brightness observed from Earth would have been between that of the full moon and Venus.

The supernova of 1054 (now designated SN1054) left a remnant which is now known as the Crab nebula. The event was the explosion of a star 4,000 light years away. This guest star was so bright that it was visible even during daylight hours for three weeks, and only disappeared from view completely two years later. Strangely, there are no European accounts of the supernova, perhaps because outside the Arab centres of learning astronomy was underdeveloped.

Far, far away

Although Chinese, Japanese, Korean and Arab astronomers recorded their observations, they did not, of course, know what the supernova was. When the next spectacular supernova display occurred in 1572, it was witnessed by Danish astronomer Tycho Brahe (1546–1601). He was the last great naked-eye astronomer; the telescope was invented a few years after his death.

Although Brahe couldn't say what the supernova was, he did make a momentous change to western astronomy on the basis of it. Up to this point the prevailing view was that of Aristotle: that the heavens are perfect and unchanging. This suited the Christian Church, as it upheld the notion of Creation by a divine being. After all, why would God create imperfect heavens that had to change?

The appearance of a new star challenged this view. The immediate assumption was that it was a tailless comet. Comets were thought to be sublunary phenomena – something that happened beneath the sphere of the Moon, so not really in the heavens and probably some kind of weather event. Tycho tried to measure the parallax of the new star; his failure to do so demonstrated that it was much further away than everyone believed.

Lucky break

Another spectacular supernova event occurred just a few years later in 1604, allowing more astronomers to view the rare event.

Like Brahe, Galileo was unable to calculate parallax for the supernova. Kepler, who had worked with Brahe, used this absence of parallax to argue that it was in the sphere of the fixed stars, further undermining the perfect-heavens position. The supernova was visible by day for three weeks and by night for 18 months. In 1941, a gas cloud remnant associated with the 1604 supernova was identified using the Mount Wilson Observatory 100-inch telescope. It is thought to be less than 20,000 light years away.

Tycho Brahe

TYCHO BRAHE (1546–1601)

Tycho (or Tyge) Brahe was born into the Danish nobility. Raised by his uncle, he travelled around Europe as a young man, studying at various universities. He became interested in astronomy and alchemy and bought astronomical instruments. He also, famously, took part in a duel with another student in 1566 and lost part of his nose. Brahe wore a metal prosthetic over the injury for the rest of his life.

Brahe returned to Denmark in 1570 and there witnessed the 'new star' of 1572 that is now the supernova remnant SN1572. Convinced that better astronomy could come only from rigorous observation, he accepted an offer from King Frederick II of Denmark to build an observatory, founding Uraniborg on the island of Hven off the coast of Copenhagen. It would become the best observatory in Europe. Brahe designed and made new instruments, trained young astronomers and ran a schedule of nightly observations that yielded the most thorough and valuable astronomical data of the age. Nightly observations might seem a fundamental requirement of an observatory, but it had been the practice of astronomers to make observations only at key points of a planet's (or the Moon's) orbit. Brahe's pattern of continuous observation revealed anomalies not previously noticed.

Eventually Frederick II died and Brahe fell out with the new king. He left Uraniborg in 1597, travelling Europe for two years before settling in Prague at the court of Emperor Rudolph II in 1599. The great German astronomer Johannes Kepler came to Prague to work with Brahe and took on the problem of working out the orbit of Mars.

Brahe was a colourful character. He kept a pet moose, which finally died after falling downstairs when he had taken it to a feast where it had drunk too much beer. Brahe's own life came to an end after another feast at which, too fastidious to cause offence by rising to relieve himself, he suffered either a bladder infection or a burst bladder and died ten days later.

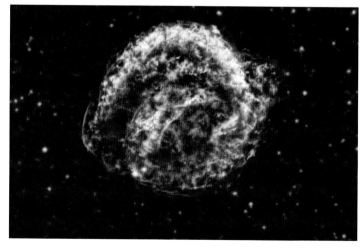

SN1604 is the remnant of Kepler's supernova, observed in 1604.

An artist's impression of the two white dwarfs of the binary system J0806 1,600 light years away. The stars are orbiting each other once every 321 seconds and growing ever closer. Currently just 80,000 km (50,000 miles) apart, they will eventually merge.

Not all supernovae within the Milky Way are visible from Earth. The most recent known supernova, named SNIa G1.9 + 0.3, occurred between 1890 and 1908 and was probably caused by two white dwarfs merging. It was discovered in 1984 from observations with the VLA telescope, but was not visible at the time because the dense cloud of gas and dust at the centre of the galaxy hid it from view. After around 120 years, the remnant is 2.6 light years across.

Although no other supernovae have been witnessed within the Milky Way, some in other galaxies have been visible to the naked eye. Because they can, briefly, shine more brightly than a whole galaxy, they can sometimes be seen. A galaxy the size of the Milky Way has a supernova about once every 50 years, but there are so many galaxies that there's about one a second somewhere in the known universe.

Working backwards

As Fan Yeh's account in AD 450 suggests, supernovae used to be given astrological rather than astronomical significance. Even Kepler made money from astrology, and apparently believed in its legitimacy. In 1604, there was no understanding of the science of the stars; they were generally considered to be lights fixed on the inside of a sphere surrounding the Earth, following the model propounded by Ptolemy (see page 105). Fruitful investigation of supernovae could only begin after the development of spectroscopy in the mid-19th century.

'The interminable wilderness of nebulae'

In the mid-19th century there was no way to distinguish between different kinds of nebulae, those cloudy objects catalogued by Messier (see page 18). Anglo-Irish astronomer William Parsons (Lord Rosse) had examined several nebulae with his 6-foot reflector telescope, which was unrivalled at the time. Even he reported in 1850 that 'the subject has become . . . more mysterious and more inapproachable'. In 1863 another English astronomer, Reverend Thomas Webb, pondered whether nebulae were not at such 'unapproachable' distances that they would never be individually resolved. Did nebulae, he wondered, indicate that some parts of the heavens are filled with a luminous fluid (milky, like the Milky Way, perhaps)? He hoped the development of ever-better telescopes would answer the questions of astronomers who found themselves 'without a guide in the interminable wilderness of nebulae'.

One difficulty was that celestial objects could only be recorded by astronomers meticulously sketching what they saw through their telescopes. When something as contentious as the apparent change in shape of a nebula was at issue, there was plenty of scope for arguing that drawings had been misinterpreted or poorly copied. The first use of photography in the study of nebulae was to record astronomers' drawings rather than the nebulae themselves. In 1880 Henry Draper took the first photograph of a nebula (Orion), but the image quality was nothing like as clear as that of an astronomer's vision through a telescope.

Shape-shifters

Many of Messier's nebulae were star clusters or galaxies. These are stable: they look the same year after year. But the nebula of a supernova changes size and shape over time. The change in the shape of some of the observed nebulae was noticed quite quickly.

Draper's 1880 photograph of the Orion nebula.

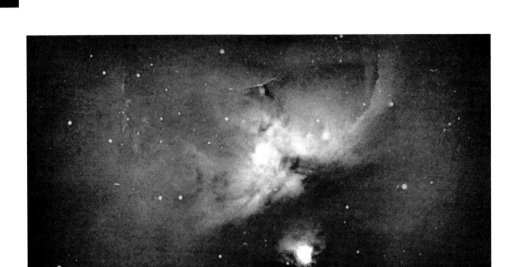

Andrew Common's photograph of the Orion nebula, M42, taken in 1883 with a long exposure.

In 1861, John Russell Hind noticed that a cluster of stars he had observed ten years previously had apparently vanished. How could this happen? The cluster or nebula had a bright star associated with it, which had first attracted Hind's attention. The star, classified as a nova ('new object'), had appeared suddenly, so close to the nebula that they seemed to be touching. Then the bright star dimmed almost to invisibility. Hind wondered if it was somehow connected with the nebula or whether the nebula could be variable, like variable stars. This new star seemed to be a variable star. Another possibility was that something dark had moved in front of the nebula, but there was no way of knowing how or what this might be. It was a puzzle.

Variable stars enter the frame

Extended observations using relatively powerful telescopes led astronomers to notice fluctuations in the brightness of some stars. In 1848, Hind discovered and charted three variable stars (including T-Tauri, which gave its name to T-Tauri stars) and noticed the fluctuations of a known star. Norman Pogson, working in India from 1861, discovered 106 variable stars, a further 21 possible variable stars and seven possible supernovae. Some of the variable stars had a puzzling association

'What food for thought, and what a field of observation undreamt of a year or two ago, have we here!... what are nebulae, since they certainly are not what our text-books describe them?... These and a thousand other questions are suggested by the scant observations we at present possess relating to the unanticipated phenomena of the variability of nebulae.'

Norman Lockyer, 1864

Left: *The young star LL Orionis surrounded by moving gas in the star nursery of the Orion nebula.*
Right: *The English astronomer John Herschel.*

with nebulae, like the one Hind observed until 1861.

In 1863, John Herschel reported that a star associated with a nebula in the southern sky had flared brightly from 1837 to 1838, grown even brighter by 1843 and begun to fade in 1850. Even more surprising, the shape of the associated nebula had changed considerably. Herschel's sketches describe a keyhole shape, but 25 years later other astronomers found that the nebula was open at the top and bottom. Herschel wrote that if the change reported could be confirmed it was 'perhaps the most startling thing which has yet occurred in sidereal astronomy'.

Reports of variable nebulae increased during the 1860s, but nothing substantial changed in terms of understanding until in 1864 the pioneer of stellar spectroscopy, William Huggins, turned his attention to novae. Huggins was coming to realize that the spectra of stars held clues to their chemical make-up and physical characteristics. He was convinced that there was a similar 'plan' throughout the universe, with the same materials and physical conditions common to all the stars. He wanted to know if nebulae shared the same conditions and whether he could discern an 'essential *physical* distinction' between them and stars. He expected perhaps a difference in temperature or density rather than in their chemical components, as he was fairly convinced that the chemical stuff of the universe was pretty universal.

Surprising stripes

Huggins began with the assumption that if nebulae are clusters of stars, their spectra should show all the chemical elements found in stars, with a continuous background of colour broken by a few dark absorption lines. If the nebulae were clouds of gas where stars might be formed, they would show the bright lines of emission spectra produced by flames and sparks.

William Huggins was a pioneer in astronomical spectroscopy.

'The reader may now be able to picture to himself to some extent the feeling of excited suspense, mingled with a degree of awe, with which, after a few moments of hesitation, I put my eye to the spectroscope. Was I not about to look into a secret place of creation?'

William Huggins, writing in 1897 of his experiences in 1864

A new nova

Huggins first turned his spectroscope successfully to the Cat's Eye nebula and what he saw surprised him utterly.

He saw a single bright line of one colour. On closer inspection he found two other single-colour lines, widely spaced. The nebula he had chosen was clearly nothing like the Sun. Looking at other planetary nebulae he found the same signature, but at first wasn't sure how to relate it to what nebulae might be. If they were star clusters, they must be clusters of stars completely unlike the Sun and the other stars he had studied.

The spectral signature suggested that the nebulae were clouds of gas or, at the very least, bodies with a gaseous photo-surface. And their composition was either a mix of hydrogen and nitrogen or some substance so far unknown on Earth. Huggins' work revealed that while some nebulae have the hallmark of stars and are likely to be star clusters (or, as it later emerged, galaxies) others have the signature of gaseous clouds.

In 1866, Huggins made the first spectroscopic observations of a nebula in the constellation Coronae Borealis. In May, Irish amateur astronomer John Birmingham had witnessed a ninth-magnitude star suddenly flare up to become a second-magnitude star. He wrote to *The Times* about it, but the paper didn't publish his letter so he sought Huggins' view on the matter. Huggins had examined the spectrum of the nova just four days earlier, when it was already fading. He found the lines characteristic of hot hydrogen, and came to a stunning conclusion. He suggested that a cataclysmic explosion might be behind the sudden burst of light produced, and exploding hydrogen gas had forced out a brilliant, glowing cloud. After just nine days, the brilliant new star had faded. The faint variable star T Coronae Borealis is now visible at the location of the supernova.

Walter Baade and Fritz Zwicky introduced the term 'supernova' in 1934 to describe the explosion rather than the remnant. Working at Mount Wilson Observatory, they observed a supernova event in the Andromeda galaxy, now named S Andromedae (SN1885A), and suggested that a supernova occurs when a star collapses into a neutron star, producing cosmic rays.

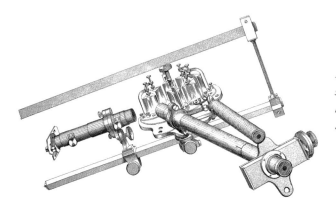

Lockyer's 'spectroscope' or spectrometer, with which he discovered helium in the Sun's atmosphere.

BIRTH OR DEATH?

Following Laplace's nebular hypothesis (see page 170), the burst of light from a nova was first interpreted as the point at which a star is born rather than its moment of death. According to this theory, when the central part of the revolving disk had enough energy to begin performing as a star, it was 'switched on' with a dramatic flash.

James Jeans had another explanation. Following his steady-state model of a universe, which was supplied with new material as necessary, he saw the nebula as a sort of port where new matter was delivered: 'the centers of the nebulae are of the nature "singular points" at which matter is poured into our universe from some other, and entirely extraneous spatial dimension, so that, to a denizen of our universe, they appear as points at which matter is being continually created.' (1928)

The CLARS observatory on Mount Wilson in southern California.

Soon afterwards, in 1938, Baade connected a nebula with a supernova remnant, suggesting that the Crab nebula was the remains of SN1054, the supernova reported by Chinese astronomers in 1054. He pointed out that although the remnant looked like a planetary nebula, the rate at which it was expanding ruled out that interpretation. He also proposed that a Type Ia supernova could be used as an indicator of distance.

STANDARD CANDLES

Standard candles are astronomical objects of known and invariable brightness. They can be used to judge distances in space, and form part of the cosmic distance scale. Type Ia supernovae and Cepheid variable stars are the most useful standard candles.

For objects up to about 100 light years away, astronomers can use parallax to calculate distance. Beyond that, up to about 10 million light years away, the luminosity of Cepheid variable stars is used. As Henrietta Leavitt demonstrated in 1912, the period (interval between bursts of brightness) of the Cepheid variables depends on the star's absolute magnitude. The more luminous stars have a longer period; and knowing a star's period enables astronomers to calculate its brightness and hence its distance.

Beyond a million light years, other methods can be used to calculate distance, including the measured brightness of a Type Ia supernova. As the actual brightness is always the same, the distance to the supernova can be calculated from its apparent brightness.

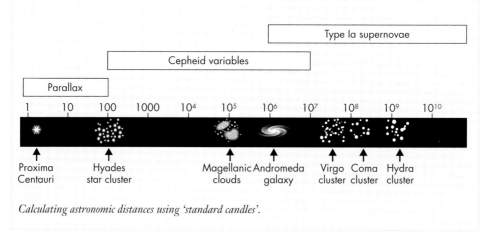

Calculating astronomic distances using 'standard candles'.

More than one type

In 1941, German-American astronomer Rudolph Minkowsky, working with Baade, categorized supernovae into two types – I and II – by their different spectral signatures. This early distinction was based on features of the spectra and not on differences in the actual nature and origins of the supernovae. Astronomers now distinguish between spectrally similar types Ia and Ib/Ic, which have very different causes.

STAY AWAY

A supernova event produces a massive amount of energy, poured into space as gamma rays. Luckily our Sun is not the type of star that will end in a supernova; but plenty of nearby stars might do so. How close could we be to a supernova and survive? Estimates of 50–100 light years' distance might make you feel more secure, though there are probably a few hundred stars that could produce supernovae within that range.

If a star, say, 30 light years from Earth ended with a supernova event, the gamma rays would probably cause mutations on Earth; they might destroy the ozone layer, produce nitrous oxide smog in the atmosphere, change the climate, and destroy the phytoplankton and reef communities that form the basis of ocean food chains. Mass extinction would be highly likely. Estimates of the frequency of such events vary from every 15 million years to every 240 million years. Earth has seen five mass extinctions, and reasons have not been identified for all of them. It remains possible that Earth has already suffered a mass extinction caused by a nearby supernova.

Currently, the top candidate for a spectacular supernova fairly nearby in our galaxy is the huge star Betelgeuse, which could implode at any time from tomorrow to a million years hence. Fortunately it's a fairly safe distance away – 430 light years – but it would put on a brilliant show. Supernovae within 600 light years of Earth are reckoned to occur less than once every 100,000 years.

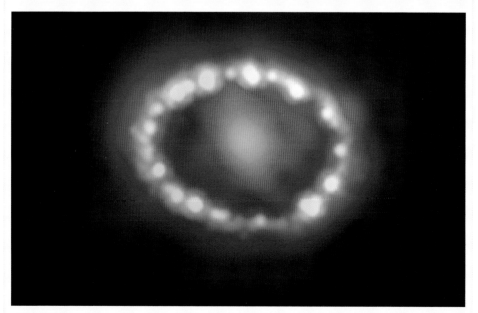

SN 1987A was the nearest supernova to Earth in hundreds of years and the brightest since 1572. It burned with 100 million times the power of the Sun.

SUPERNOVAE

Type I supernova

This type of nova takes place in binary star systems, with at least one of the stars classified as a white dwarf.

One star accretes material from its counterpart, accumulating mass as a result. This eventually incites a chain nuclear reaction.

The nuclear reaction culminates in the star reaching critical density, when it explodes in a supernova. Beams of gamma radiation can also be emitted.

Type II supernova

After losing the ability to stably fuse heavy elements, the star can no longer retain a gravitational equilibrium, thus the core collapses in on itself.

The core rebounds in quick succession, subsequently releasing the outer layers of gas out into space, forming a nebula.

After the dust settles, a neutron star or black hole is left behind (which one will depend on the star's mass).

Type Ia, used as a standard candle, is the result of two objects interacting. A white dwarf steals material from a companion, so it becomes hot enough to start fusing carbon. It goes into a phase of nuclear fusion that in a few seconds leads to the catastrophic collapse of the star. The burst of luminosity is consistently of magnitude -19.3 (five billion times as bright as the Sun). Type Ib/c supernovae are produced by the collapse of massive Wolf–Rayet stars (giant stars that have fused all their hydrogen and are fusing helium or heavier elements).

In 1946, Fred Hoyle first proposed what was going on inside a supernova. He suggested that the nuclear fusion of heavy elements removed enough energy from the system for gravitational collapse to become possible. The star would become unstable and expel elements into interstellar space. Later, in the 1960s, Hoyle and William Fowler further explored the idea of rapid nuclear fusion powering a supernova.

When a supernova in the Large Magellanic Cloud was noticed within hours of it starting in 1987, astronomers watched its development and aftermath, confirming theories about supernova formation.

After the firestorm

The supernova is the end of life for a main-sequence star (or pair of stars), but it's also the start of something new. The collapse itself involves such a massive amount of energy and pressure that types of nuclear synthesis which were not possible in the

HALF BY HALF

Radioactive substances change by losing energy in one of several forms. There are three types of radiation: alpha particles, beta particles and gamma rays. Alpha particles are helium nuclei: two protons and two neutrons. Beta particles are high-energy electrons (or positrons). Gamma rays are photons acting as waves. When an atom loses an alpha particle, its atomic number changes so it becomes a different element.

Rutherford noticed that different radioactive elements decay at different rates. Their decay rate is specified in the form of the half-life – the length of time it takes for half of the atoms in a sample of the substance to decay. The half-lifes of radioactive elements range from tiny fractions of a second to longer than the age of the universe.

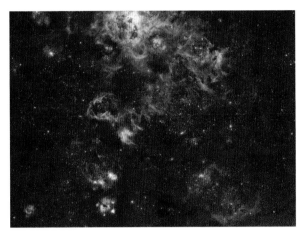

SN 1987A is on the outskirts of this massive nebula.

heart of a star can begin. The fusion of iron, which requires (rather than releases) energy, can be accomplished in the high-energy environment of a supernova. Heavier elements, including gold, plutonium and uranium, are also produced. These join the interstellar medium and become available in the molecular clouds which will form the next generation of stars. The Earth and everything on it, including our own bodies, is made from atoms forged either in the hearts of stars or blasted into existence in their cataclysmic death throes.

This is not to say that every atom of an element heavier than iron was definitely forged in a supernova. Some elements are produced by the radioactive decay of other elements and come about over time. Of the 118 elements known today, 92 are naturally found on Earth. The others have been forced into existence in particle accelerators, but might also be produced in extreme conditions in supernovae or by radioactive decay.

Radioactive decay is the falling apart of atomic nuclei. Radioactivity was first observed by Becquerel (see page 82) when he was examining the behaviour of uranium salts. Uranium is a primordial nuclide, a type of nucleus that was around when the Earth formed at the start of the solar system. There are 253 stable nuclides, which are versions of the non-radioactive elements – they don't change. There are more stable nuclides than there are total elements because some elements exist in different isotopes (different nuclear configurations). In addition, there are 33 non-stable (radioactive) nuclides.

The current composition of the Earth can't reveal to us all that might be created in a supernova. For one thing, our solar system is just a single example of a Population I star and its entourage of planets, and we are looking at a snapshot of it 4.55 billion years after its formation. If we were to look at a planet that had formed 10 billion years ago, some of the non-stable nuclides might have disappeared. If we were to look at a planet created only a few million years ago, we might see nuclides which have long since decayed on Earth and changed into something else.

For example, if any lead-212 was created in a supernova that fed into our solar system, we would never find it. Lead-212 has a half-life of just 10.6 hours. It decays into bismuth-212, which itself has a half-life of only an hour, decaying into polonium-212

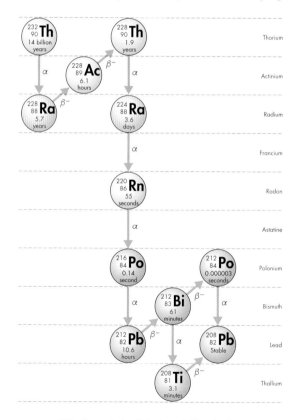

The decay chain of thorium-232 to lead-208.

or thallium-208. Polonium's half-life is less than a millionth of a second, and thallium's is just over three minutes. Both decay into lead-208, the stable isotope of the lead that is plentiful on Earth. We can't tell by looking at the lead whether it was created in a supernova as lead-208 or whether it is the product of a decay chain.

Other elements decay very slowly. Tellurium-128 has a half-life of 2.2×10^{24} years, or about 160 trillion times the age of the universe. It's so stable that if the Pilgrim Fathers had taken a gram of tellurium-128 to North America in 1620, there's a pretty good chance that not even a single atom would have decayed yet.

The short chain from lead-212 to lead-208 comes towards the end of the decay of thorium-232, a primordial nuclide with a half-life of 14 billion years (about the age of the universe). Any thorium-232 created by a Population III or II star going supernova would largely be still around, but a fair amount could already be lead-208. After thorium, the link in the chain with the longest half-life is radium-228, which has a half-life of 5.7 years. Once the decay chain gets going, an atom is likely to reach the end quite quickly.

This means that when we examine the elements around us on Earth (or on another planet, or even in another solar system or galaxy) we might find they come from a number of sources: forged in the heart of a star, or in a supernova blast, or the result of radioactive decay. Radioactive decay can also be triggered by the action of cosmic rays on elements that are otherwise in a relatively stable environment.

Left behind

The explosion of a supernova lasts only seconds or minutes. Material is blasted away into space, travelling at immense speeds on a journey that will take thousands, millions or even billions of years until it is incorporated into another star. In the meantime it becomes part of the interstellar medium. But the collapsed core of the star is left behind.

Dark star

As we have seen, the pressure at the heart of the collapsed star is so immense that the matter can be crushed to neutrons. In another scenario,

Of the 33 primordial radionuclides found on Earth, only four have a half-life shorter than or equal to the age of the universe. The rest have very long half-lifes.

CHAPTER 6

with an even larger initial star, it can be compressed so far that it becomes a black hole. Interestingly, 'dark stars' and black holes were theorized long before we knew anything about the mechanisms of a supernova.

The English clergyman John Michell first suggested the possibility of a phenomenon now known as black holes in 1784. Michell was a brilliant scientist who made astonishing predictions in several fields. He was so far ahead of the curve that his ideas were not taken up at the time. He made advances in seismology and magnetism and was the first person to apply statistical analysis to astronomy, finding that the occurrence of dual and multi-star systems was far greater than would occur randomly, and explaining their existence as a result of mutual gravitational attraction.

Michell's work on black holes relied initially on Newton's theory that light is made of tiny particles rather than waves of energy. (Today we think of light as quanta – tiny packets of energy – with both wave-like and particle-like properties.) Michell suggested that light should also be subject to the pull of gravity and that gravity would slow down the movement of light from a star which had a lot of mass. He extrapolated this to suggest that if a star were so massive that the escape velocity for light particles

was greater than the speed of light, the light could never leave and the star would be invisible – a 'dark star'. He calculated that a star the density of the Sun would need to have 500 times the Sun's mass to trap its light. Michell went on to suggest that although we would be unable

'If there should really exist in nature any bodies, whose density is not less than that of the Sun, and whose diameters are more than 500 times the diameter of the Sun . . . or if there should exist any other bodies of a somewhat smaller size, which are not naturally luminous . . . if any other luminous bodies should happen to revolve about them we might still perhaps from the motions of these revolving bodies infer the existence of the central ones with some degree of probability.'

John Michell, 1783

to detect the dark star directly, we might be able to infer its presence from the movement of objects nearby that were affected by its gravity – in particular, the movement of a companion star (see quote above). Black holes can be detected in exactly this way today, and all the stellar black holes tentatively identified in the Milky Way are part of a binary system with a normal star.

Where Michell was mistaken was in his plan for measuring the mass of stars by calculating the speed of light leaving them. But even here he was edging towards a modern method. He supposed that the pull of gravity would slow down the light leaving the stars, and believed that if he could measure the speed of the light, he would be able to calculate the mass

An artist's impression of the area around a supermassive black hole at the heart of the galaxy NGC 3783. There is a ring of glowing hot dust around the black hole.

of the star. He was wrong because the speed of light is invariable.

As fast as light, but never faster

In the 1660s, Isaac Newton measured the speed of sound, arriving at a value within 15 per cent of the true value. However, most people considered it would be impossible to measure the speed of light. It was thought that it was probably infinite, with light arriving at its destination instantaneously (as it appears to) or at least so fast that it could never be measured.

Only a short time later, in 1676, Danish physicist Ole Rømer succeeded in measuring the speed of light – but he did so by accident. Rømer was timing and recording the eclipse of Jupiter's moon Io in the hope of deriving a method of calculating longitude (the method had been suggested by Galileo). After making observations for many years, Rømer realized that when Earth was farthest from Jupiter in its orbit around the Sun, the eclipse occurred about eleven minutes later than average and when Earth was closest to Jupiter around six months later, the eclipse came about eleven minutes earlier. He realized that the difference could be accounted for if the speed of light was, after all, finite. It was taking light 22 minutes to cross the diameter of Earth's orbit around the Sun. To calculate the speed of light, he needed only to divide the diameter of the orbit by 22 minutes.

Dutch scientist Christiaan Huygens did the first calculation, returning a speed of 211,000 km (131,000 miles) per second. This falls short of the actual figure of 299,000 km (186,000 miles) per second, because Rømer had wrongly estimated the difference in time between the eclipses and had an inaccurate figure for Earth's orbit, but it was close enough to be useful. More importantly, it settled the question of whether the speed of light is finite.

In 1728, James Bradley made a better measurement working from the apparent

·1644· *Ole Rømer* ·1710·

Ole Rømer was working at the Paris Observatory when he measured the speed of light in 1676. He failed to persuade the director of the Observatory that light travels at a finite speed.

displacement of the stars caused by Earth's movement around the Sun. His figure of 301,000 km (187,000 miles) per second is remarkably close to the currently accepted value of 299,792,458 km (186,282,397 miles) per second. It will now never change, as the standard metre is defined by the speed of light: a metre is the distance light travels in a vacuum in one 299,792,458th of a second. In 1905, Einstein proposed that the speed of light is always the same no matter where the observer is standing and whether or not the observed object is moving. He said that nothing can travel faster than the speed of light.

Light doesn't always travel at the speed of light, though. It travels more slowly through air or water than through a vacuum. Research in 2015 also found, surprisingly, that the structure of light can affect its speed, slowing it down. The speed of light should then be considered an upper limit rather than an absolute constant. There is also speculation that the speed of light might not have had the same value at all times in the past. If this turns out to be the case, our calculations of the size of the universe are likely to be wrong.

Black holes again

Michell was not the only person to propose the existence of stars from which no light could escape. French scientist Pierre-Simon Laplace mentioned the possibility in 1796, although without initially presenting any mathematics to support the idea: 'The gravitation attraction of a star with a diameter 250 times that of the Sun and comparable in density to the Earth would be so great no light could escape from its surface. The largest bodies in the universe may thus be invisible by reason of their magnitude.'

A visualization of material whirling around a supermassive black hole near the centre of the Milky Way. The gas is thought to be travelling at 30 per cent of the speed of light.

From theory to fact

Laplace seems to have worked independently and without knowledge of Michell's work. There was little scientific communication between the almost-warring states of Britain and France at the time, and it was not easy working in revolutionary France. Michell's proposal was almost an aside to his work on binary and triple star systems. Oddly, both he and Laplace were aware that a non-luminous star could either be much larger than the Sun (and therefore have immense gravity) or much smaller than the Sun but a lot denser; yet neither pursued the second option. This, though, is the case for the black holes known today: they are physically small but incredibly dense. A black hole the diameter of New York City would have around ten times the mass of the Sun.

The German physicist Karl Schwarzschild achieved his greatest work while serving on the Russian front in World War I.

Of light and blackness

During the 19th century, Newton's notion of light as 'corpuscular' was replaced by the idea that light is a wave of energy.

It appeared that a wave of energy was less likely to be affected by gravity, so the possibility of finding black holes receded. But in 1899 Max Planck explained that energy is divided into tiny packets called quanta. The amount of energy produced by any electromagnetic source is a constrained value and is given by the equation:

energy = frequency x Planck constant (or $E = hv$)

Einstein's theory of special relativity put this calculation to good use in 1905. It soon became the basis of quantum mechanics and revolutionized physics and cosmology. If light is treated as quanta, it can be deflected by gravity. This was definitively demonstrated by Eddington using the eclipse of 1919 (see page 70).

One result of Einstein's general relativity equation was that it confirmed Michell's idea that a sufficiently dense body could

> 'This velocity is so nearly that of light that it seems we have strong reason to conclude that light itself (including radiant heat and other radiations if any) is an electromagnetic disturbance in the form of waves.'
>
> James Clerk Maxwell, 1885

prevent the escape even of light. Just months after Einstein published his theory in 1915, German physicist and astronomer Karl Schwarzschild proposed that a black hole is defined by a kind of boundary called the event horizon. Anything on the black hole's side of the boundary cannot escape, whether it is matter or energy. It's a gravitational point of no return, and anything that crosses the event horizon becomes part of the black hole, irretrievably. The distance of the event horizon from the centre of the black hole is called the Schwarzschild radius. In fact, everything with mass has a Schwarzschild radius: that of the Earth is about 9 mm. The centre point of a black hole is a singularity: a point at which space-time curvature is infinite. The volume of the point (in a non-rotating black hole) or disk-shaped smear (in a rotating black hole) is zero, but as it contains all the mass of the black hole, its density is infinite.

BEING NOWHERE

Writing in 1926, Arthur Eddington commented on the density of large stars and the possibility of their mass being crammed into their Schwarzschild radius. Einstein's equation, he said, ruled out extremely dense large stars. He pointed out that a large star such as Betelgeuse would not be visible if it were even as dense as the Sun, since 'the force of gravitation would be so great that light would be unable to escape from it, the rays falling back to the star like a stone to the earth. Secondly, the red shift of the spectral lines would be so great that the spectrum would be shifted out of existence. Thirdly, the mass would produce so much curvature of the space-time metric that space would close up around the star, leaving us outside (i.e., nowhere)'. His final point is, disappointingly, not true.

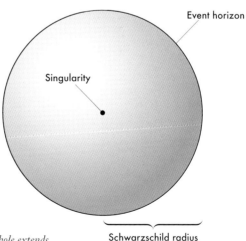

The Schwarzschild radius of a black hole extends from its centre (the singularity) to its event horizon.

Event horizon

Singularity

Schwarzschild radius

$$R = \frac{2GM}{c^2}$$

Size limits

In 1931, Indian astrophysicist Subrahmanyan Chandrasekhar worked out that a non-rotating white dwarf above a certain mass – now called the Chandrasekhar limit – is unstable and will collapse in on itself. That mass is about 1.4 times the mass of the Sun. In fact, a white dwarf over the Chandrasekhar limit collapses into a neutron star, which is then stable. Another limit, predicted by Robert Oppenheimer and others in 1939, states that if neutron stars exceed the TOV (Tolman–Oppenheimer–Volkoff) limit, they will collapse into black holes. Calculations of the limiting mass ranged from the first value of 0.7 times the mass of the Sun to up to three times its mass,

FROZEN STARS

Oppenheimer and his colleagues posited that time stops at the event horizon of a black hole. Unless an observer was falling into a black hole (in which case the science of it would be the least of their worries), time would seem to stop at the event horizon. As no light can escape from it, the surface of the collapsed star would always appear as it did at the moment it crossed the Schwarzschild radius. For this reason, black holes were called 'frozen stars'.

The Black Hole of Calcutta (Kolkota) was a small prison in Fort William, Kolkota, where a large number of British and Indian prisoners were kept in airless, overheated conditions for three days in 1756. Most of the prisoners died from suffocation, dehydration or trampling (reports of the numbers vary).

but the observation of two neutron stars colliding in 2017 has suggested a value of 2.17 times the mass of the Sun.

Theory solidifies

Einstein thought black holes could never exist and many scientists followed his lead. It was not until the 1960s that sufficient believers had enough mathematical evidence to persuade more sceptical physicists of the reality of black holes. In particular, English physicists Stephen Hawking and Roger Penrose showed that in certain circumstances the existence of a black hole becomes inevitable.

The name 'black hole' was first used in the 1960s, though its exact origins are uncertain. John Michell had referred to dark stars, but scientists of the early 20th century preferred the more prosaic 'gravitationally collapsed object'. In the early 1960s, the physicist Robert Dicke apparently likened the objects to the 'black hole of Calcutta', a prison from which it was rumoured no one ever escaped. The term was used in print in 1963.

The first black hole to be detected was Cygnus X-1, about 6,000 light years away. It was first spotted as a source of radiation in 1964 by rockets carrying Geiger counters to measure radioactivity. Further investigation with more sensitive equipment in 1971 found strong radio emissions coming from the direction of HDE 226868, a blue super-giant. But this star could not itself produce the signals seen, so astronomers concluded it had a dark partner. The situation could be explained by a black hole orbiting the star at a distance of 0.2 AU (a fifth of the distance from Earth to the Sun). At around 15 times the mass of the Sun, the object's mass is too great for even the largest neutron star, so astronomers decided that it's most likely a black hole. The black hole 'feeds' on material it pulls from the giant star. In 1974, Stephen Hawking famously bet fellow astronomer Kip Thorne that it would turn out not to be a black hole – a bet he conceded in 1990 when more detailed data made other explanations unlikely.

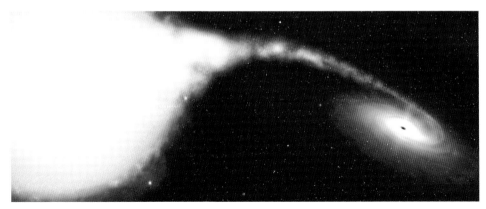

In this artist's concept, the black hole Cygnus X-1 (right) pulls material from its giant neighbour, HDE 226868. The material accumulates in a spinning disk, the accretion disk, as it accelerates toward the event horizon of the black hole.

SPAGHETTIFICATION

There has been much consideration of what would happen if someone were pulled into a black hole. In 1988, Stephen Hawking coined the term 'spaghettification' for the process by which the victim's body would be stretched to a long, thin string as gravity acted on the end approaching the black hole first. Rather obviously, being spaghettified isn't good for you. But it's likely that the person would burn up at the event horizon instead, a result suggested in 2012. It's a bit more mundane, but either way the lesson has to be: 'don't play too close to a black hole'.

No escape, but . . .

The conventional model of a black hole under Einstein's relativity theory makes it impossible for anything to escape from it, and this makes black holes invisible. But they often appear to have two jets coming from them, perpendicular to the accretion disk of matter drawn inwards and circling the black hole, going faster and faster. As matter is pulled into the black hole, it loses gravitational potential energy which is released as particles streaming out. So it's not escaping from within the event horizon of the black hole, but being ejected at the event horizon. It's made a lucky escape, just in time.

Holes, big and small

The black holes created in the aftermath of large stars going supernova are called stellar black holes. There are also super-massive black holes which, as the name suggests, are much larger. They are found at the very heart of a galaxy, and possibly of all galaxies. No one is entirely sure how they form; it's possible that they are made by smaller black holes colliding and combining, or made directly in the super-dense core of the galactic cloud. The largest black

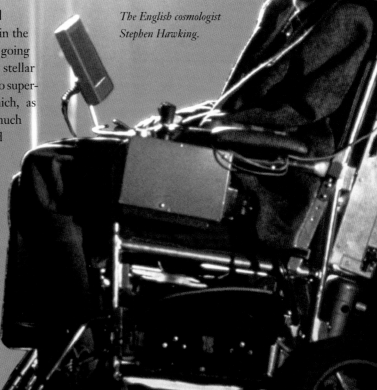

The English cosmologist Stephen Hawking.

An artist's impression of the most known distant quasar, ULAS J1120+0641. It is powered by a black hole (which is not visible) with a mass two billion times the mass of the Sun. This is how it might have looked 770 million years after the Big Bang.

hole found so far has 66 billion times the mass of the Sun and is at the heart of the quasar called TON 618. (The quasar is the energetically active accretion disk, pouring out light.) The black hole has a Schwarzschild radius of 1,300 AU and the quasar is one of the brightest objects in the known universe. Quasars can even cluster together, forming Large Quasar Groups (LQGs), which are among the biggest structures in the universe. The imaginatively named Huge LQG, discovered in 2013, is four billion light years across at its widest point.

The biggest stellar black hole is M33 X-7, about 3 million light years from the Milky Way in the galaxy M33. Its mass is nearly 16 times that of the Sun and its companion star is 70 times the mass of the Sun, making the pair the largest known binary system with a black hole. The smallest stellar black hole, discovered in 1992, is GRO J0422+32. Its mass was originally calculated at 3.7 to 5 times the mass of the Sun, but a calculation in 2012 put it at just 2.1 times the Sun's mass. This is smaller than the upper limit for the size of a neutron star (2.7 times the mass of the Sun), so raises the question of whether it is

a black hole at all or something else. There is little evidence for black holes between the very large examples at the heart of a galaxy and the stellar black holes produced by supernovae.

Forging ahead

After its first round of creating stars which then rapidly destroyed themselves, the universe fell into a pattern by which clouds of matter condensed into new stars of varying sizes which fused hydrogen until they exhausted their supply. The exhausted stars came to dramatic or less dramatic ends and released their products of nuclear fusion to be incorporated into the next generation of stars.

Smaller stars have not yet exhausted their supplies and will continue on the main sequence for a long time. This looks like a stable pattern; but there is a difference between the formation of stars from metal-rich material and that of stars from a primordial mix of hydrogen and helium. Once there are more elements available, they can be incorporated into a new type of body: planets. Population II and I stars both had the wherewithal to build planets.

CHAPTER 7

MAKING WORLDS

'What a wonderful and amazing Scheme
have we here of the magnificent Vastness of the
Universe! So many Suns, so many Earths, and
every one of them stock'd with so many Herbs,
Trees and Animals, and adorn'd with so many
Seas and Mountains!'

Christiaan Huygens, 1698
(published posthumously)

**As the stars burst into life, there was
still much material swirling around
them. From this debris, planets could
form. We only know about our own
system of planets in any detail, but we
can extrapolate from it to think about
the many worlds that lie beyond our
solar system. We can see how they form
by observing distant systems as well as
trawling our own for evidence.**

The inner planets of the solar system and their orbits.

An artist's impression of a 'super-Earth' exoplanet orbiting the star HD 85512. The planet is on the edge of the star's habitable zone.

Burning bright

The very first planets formed within a billion years of the Big Bang, immediately recycling the material from the expired first stars. The oldest known planet, nicknamed Methuselah, is around 13 billion years old, so planet building started early in the story of the universe.

Although we are aware of exoplanets around other stars, we can only glimpse them from afar and have no way of tracing their history. For extrapolation from our own solar system to be valid we have to be confident that ours is fairly typical of systems that could be found elsewhere.

In earlier times, when religious views predominated in modelling the universe, Earth and the Sun were privileged as the places made by God to hold his greatest creation, humankind. Some of the Ancient Greeks, including the Pythagoreans, believed that the stars were other worlds but that our own world was unique. By the beginning of the 17th century, the idea that our world is one of many was gaining ground.

The notion that Earth doesn't enjoy a privileged position in the universe is known as the Copernican principle, though it has little to do with Copernicus. The Italian philosopher and cleric Giordano Bruno was one of the first to state categorically (and dangerously) that our privileged position is an illusion and Earth is just one of many other worlds. He was burned for heresy in 1600, partly because of this view which had been a named and recognized heresy since at least the time of St Augustine (AD 345–430). A mere 20 years later Johannes Kepler published a diagram which showed the world attached to one of

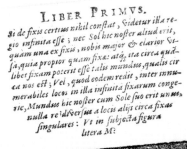

Kepler's diagram in his Epitome
astronomiae Copernicanae (1618–21)
shows the world, represented by M for
'mundus', as one of any number of
similar stars.

'Who are we? We find that
we live on an insignificant
planet of a humdrum star
lost in a galaxy tucked
away in some forgotten
corner of a universe in
which there are far more
galaxies than people.'
Carl Sagan, 1980

many identical stars. British astrophysicist Michael Rowan-Robinson (b.1942) has suggested that adopting the Copernican principle is the marker of modern thought, since 'no well-informed and rational person can imagine that the Earth occupies a unique position in the universe.'

In the early 20th century, Dutch astronomer Jacobus Kapteyn's studies of the proper movement of stars revealed they tend to travel in one of two opposite directions. This was the first evidence that the Milky Way rotates, though he did not recognize it. His observations led him to the conclusion that the Milky Way is about 40,000 light years across and the solar system is near the centre, offset by just 2,000 light years. In 1917, Harlow Shapley revealed we are not, in fact, near the centre of the Milky Way but stuck out on one of the arms. It was found in the 1920s that the Milky Way is 100,000 light years across and we are a full 40,000 light years from the centre of it.

Junk modelling in space

As we have seen, stars form as clouds of dust and gas collapsing under great pressure; the core eventually becomes so dense that nuclear fusion begins. Around 12.5–13 billion years ago, the universe had the wherewithal to make something other than balls of gas.

So far, we have concentrated on the dense clump of matter that collapses to produce a star. But not all the matter involved in the collapse ends up in the middle. The current theory for how the remaining matter comes to form planets, moons, asteroids and other bodies is called the solar nebular disk model. It was outlined by Soviet astrophysicist Victor Safronov in 1969 (see page 170) and further developed over the following decades. As the centre collapses, the cloud churns. As it is compressed more and more, the churning motion becomes rotation, with most of the cloud revolving in the same direction. The process continues and over time the rotating cloud flattens to a disk, in much the same way as a lump of pizza dough, constantly turned, flattens out to a pizza base. The result is a protoplanetary disk surrounding the central star. It takes about 100,000 years for the first stage of collapse to produce a disk and a visible T-Tauri star. The star continues to pull in material and the disk endures for around 10 million years (the oldest known is 25 million years old). Within the disk, planets and other objects form from the dust and continue to orbit the central star. Eventually, solar wind from the star blows away material in the disk that has not been used and the result is a neat arrangement of planets and other objects orbiting the star in space that is otherwise pretty much empty.

Until very recently, astronomers could only look at a snapshot of the current state of our own solar system to find clues to how planets form. With the launch of the

THE DUST SETTLES

Hubble images show that the star Beta Pictoris has several belts of planetesimals. In the early 1990s they also revealed dark disks of dust swirling around young stars in the Orion nebula, a region of star formation. Hubble images of the star AB Aurigae show a developing system from above the disk, so we can see the whole of it circling the star. This is an earlier stage in the system's development, when the star is just 2–4 million years old. There are bright patches which are thought to be concentrations of matter in the process of becoming planets.

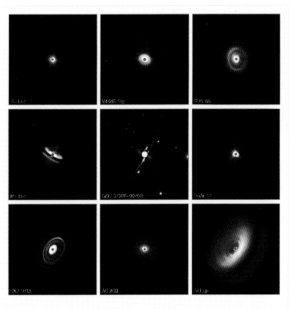

Images from the ESO's Very Large Telescope showing various shapes of young stars surrounded by disks of dust.

Hubble Space Telescope in 1990 it became possible to see into the protoplanetary disks of other stars. We have even been able to examine pristine material from the dawn of the solar system, most recently with a flyby of a Kuiper Belt object in 2019.

From disk to lumps

Planet formation takes millions of years. Consequently we will never be able to monitor a planetary system as it grows from dust and gas. Instead we must piece the process together by looking at different stages of planetary formation drawn from wherever we can find them.

A protoplanetary disk typically has a radius of around 1,000 AU, but is vertically very thin. In 1984, using a land-based telescope, a protoplanetary disk was first seen. It encircles the star Beta Pictoris, 63.4 light years away. At only 20–26 million years old, the star is young.

Within a protoplanetary disk, matter begins to stick together as it collides. Chunks grow as their increasing mass is accompanied by increasing gravity, so they attract more matter. Large lumps crash into one another, sometimes shattering and scattering their pieces and sometimes colliding gently enough to stick together to form a large lump. Hundreds of collections of matter circling the star accrue over millions of years. These are planetesimals – baby planets.

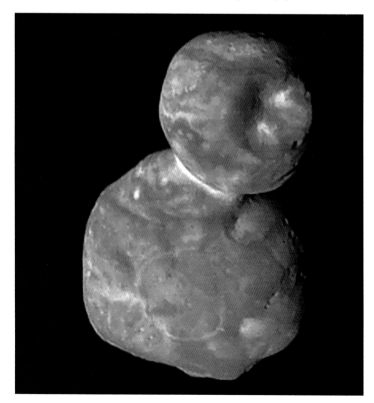

Photographed here by the New Horizons mission in 2019, Ultima Thule is a contact pair of objects in the Kuiper Belt. The larger object is only 19 km (12 miles) across and the smaller just 14 km (9 miles) across. They form a planetesimal, frozen in time, from the earliest years of the solar system.

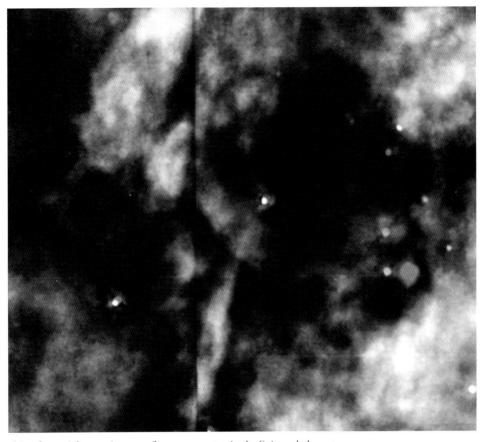

A jet of material streaming away from a young star in the Orion nebula.

Planetesimals grow by accreting material which strays across their path and by sweeping up anything in their orbit. Some of them coalesce with other planetissimals or are smashed apart in collisions, until eventually there is a stable number of planets, each of which has cleared its orbit of other matieral. The star HD141569, five million years old, has a gap in its disk of dust which suggests that a forming planet has already carved out its own orbital path. This was discovered in 1999 from Hubble images.

Not all the material of the protoplanetary disk ends up being incorporated into planets. There are plenty of other bodies in our solar system, including moons, asteroids, dwarf planets and comets, and there is no reason to suppose that this is not the case in other solar systems.

Beta Pictoris is known to have comets and at least one planet, named (unimaginatively) Beta Pictoris b. Hubble images of the star reveal a second disk overlapping the first, offset by about 4° from the plane of the main disk. The planet's gravitational force seems

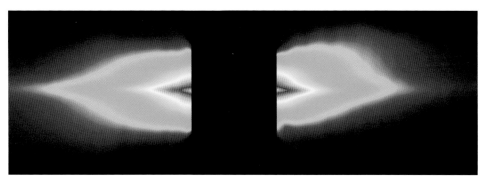

A false colour image of the dust disk around the star Beta Pictoris.

to have pulled dust and gas from the main disk into its own orbit, making the second disk. The matter could accrete into the planet, or perhaps form a moon around it.

Tadpoles

If a star has enough space to spread its protoplanetary disk without interference, it can grow planets. But some stars form too close to others, or near concentrations of gas moving in the same direction. Hubble has photographed stars with protoplanetary disks distorted by nearby stars. Some of these resemble tadpoles, with a fat end near the star and a thinner end trailing away like a comet. Harsh radiation and streams of charged particles from another nearby star push the disk away from its own star. It is difficult for a star with a disk distorted in this way to form planets. Even so, Hubble has detected gravel-sized clumps forming in a 'tadpole' just one million years old. Planets might be able to form if they can do so quickly, before the material in the disk is blown away into space by its aggressive neighbour.

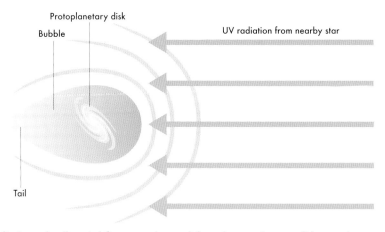

Intense radiation and stellar wind from a nearby star deform the protoplanetary disk around a new star.

Planets in close-up

As we have already seen, the current theory that the solar system formed out of the material of a protoplanetary disk is not the only hypothesis there has been.

Putting the Sun at the centre

Until the end of the 16th century, throughout the Middle East and the West, the predominant model of the solar system was the one suggested by the Ancient Greeks, which was subsequently refined and popularized by Ptolemy in the 2nd century AD. It was a geocentric system that placed a stationary Earth at the centre of the universe, with the Moon, Sun, other planets and 'fixed stars' moving around it. Each heavenly body was fixed to a crystalline sphere which rotated, carrying the planet, Moon or Sun as a passenger, although the

AN IMPIOUS IDEA

Although the geocentric model held sway for nearly 2,000 years, an Ancient Greek philosopher called Aristarchus (c.310–c.230 BC) had proposed that the Earth rotates on its own axis and is in motion around the Sun. It was considered an impious notion. Aristotle noted that if Aristarchus was correct, the universe must be very large as there is no noticeable parallax in the position of the fixed stars. This, for Aristotle, was a good enough reason to reject Aristarchus's idea. For everyone else, Aristotle's disapproval was a good enough reason to reject a heliocentric (Sun-centred) model.

For the Christian Church, the suggestion that the Earth was at the centre of the solar system (and, indeed, the universe) fitted well with the belief that God had created it as a home for humans. It was also consistent with what we see when we look upwards: objects seem to move relative to the Earth and they look a lot smaller than the Earth, so even on the simplest level the model is quite persuasive. For the Church, however, it became an article of faith and it was eventually declared heretical to suggest otherwise.

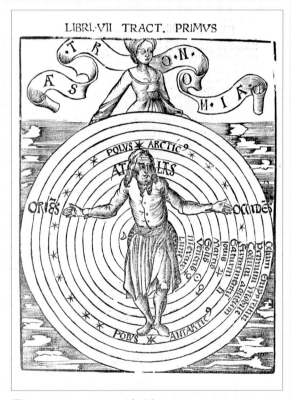

The geocentric universe, with Atlas at its centre.

fixed stars were thought to be on an outer sphere which rotated in its entirety.

The geocentric model didn't consider how the heavenly bodies had come to be, besides assuming they were put there by a divinity. The first serious challenge to the geocentric model came from Polish astronomer Nicolaus Copernicus in 1542. He suggested that the Sun sits at the centre of the solar system, with the Earth and other planets in orbit around it. As with the geocentric model, in Copernicus' version the Moon still orbits the Earth.

A problem with the geocentric model was that if we observe the planets rigorously and plot their movement, they periodically seem to move backwards in a loop, before moving forwards again. This is called retrograde motion. Astronomers and mathematicians constructed circles, called epicycles, within the orbit, so that their models matched observations. Copernicus recognized that the apparent retrograde motion is a result of Earth's own movement around the Sun. If we were able to observe the motions of the planets from the surface of the Sun, they would simply orbit in a normal way.

Copernicus first distributed his ideas in hand-written form in 1514, but didn't publish them until two months before his death in 1543. Diplomatically, he dedicated his book, *De revolutionibus orbium coelestium (On the Revolutions of the Heavenly Spheres)* to the Pope, Paul III. Without Copernicus's permission, and possibly without his knowledge, a preface was added which suggested that the model within was a convenient way of thinking about planetary movements, one that facilitated astronomical calculation, rather than a literal account of the state of the heavens. This protected the book from immediate condemnation, although it was eventually banned in 1616.

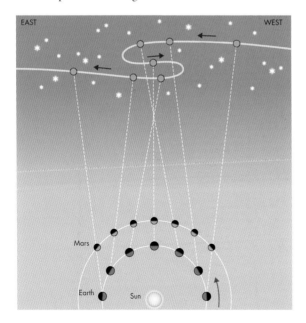

The apparent retrograde movement of the planets is a result of the different orbital speeds of Earth and the other planets.

From circle to ellipse

Copernicus's model still did not allow perfectly accurate mapping of the movement of the planets. He continued to assert that the heavenly bodies move in perfect circles (this had been insisted upon by Aristotle, who saw the circle as the perfect shape). In 1609, all the pieces fell into place.

Johannes Kepler published the laws he had deduced from examining planetary motion. These were based principally on the observations of Tycho Brahe, who had made the most detailed and precise record of the motion of Mars that had ever been attempted. His data led Kepler to realize that the planets follow elliptical rather than circular orbits around the Sun.

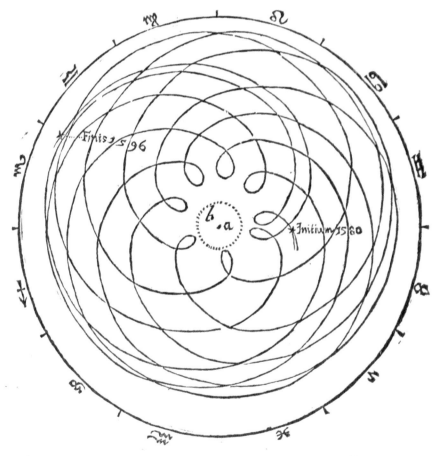

The movements of Mars as mapped by Tycho Brahe from 1580 to 1596, published by Johannes Kepler in Astronomia nova *in 1609.*

JOHANNES KEPLER (1571–1630)

Born into relative poverty in Swabia, now in southwest Germany, Johannes Kepler was sickly as a child but survived to go to university in Tübingen where he first studied to become a Lutheran minister. That was not to be his destiny, however. He studied with the great astronomer and mathematician Michael Mästlin (1550–1631), who officially taught him the Ptolemaic model of the universe but also introduced him to Copernicus's radical theory that the Earth moves around the Sun.

KEPPLER.

*From a Picture in the Collection of
Godfrey Kneeres Merchant at Potsdam*

From 1594, Kepler was employed as a mathematician and calendar-maker (an important application of astronomy at the time). In 1596 he took the risky move of writing his first defence of the Copernican universe. Neither the Lutheran nor the Catholic Church approved of the model, although it had not yet been ruled heretical. Nevertheless, Kepler and his wife invented a code which they used to communicate with each other so that their dangerous ideas could not readily be made public.

Mästlin thought Kepler could improve the rather esoteric cosmological model he had proposed in *Mysterium cosmographicum* (*Mysteries of the cosmos)* if he had better data to draw on. Mästlin sent Kepler's work to Tycho Brahe, the foremost astronomer of his day, and in 1600 Kepler went to work with Brahe in Prague. He was set the task of untangling the complex motion of Mars, which Kepler optimistically expected to complete in eight days.

When Brahe died the following year, Kepler inherited his job as Imperial Mathematician, along with his data. (This event was so opportune for Kepler that he was later suspected of poisoning Brahe, whose body was exhumed in 1901 and again in 2010. The first time, traces of mercury seemed to point to Kepler's guilt, but the later examination found the levels too low to suggest poisoning.) After eight years of research, Kepler realized that if the planets have elliptical orbits and Earth's own movement is taken into account, the apparent retrograde path of Mars is explained. He published his radical findings in 1609.

Kepler published his fullest account of the mechanics of the solar system in 1621 in *Epitome Astronomiae Copernicanae*. He went on to complete the *Rudolphine Tables*, which Brahe had long wanted to produce. They provided a way of calculating the positions of the planets at any point in the future. Kepler died in 1630, while travelling.

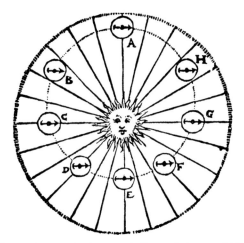

Kepler imagined a form of magnetic attraction between the Sun and planets, which regulated their orbits.

Kepler's book *Astronomia nova (The new astronomy)* set out his first two laws of planetary motion:

1. All planets orbit the Sun in elliptical orbits, with the Sun at one focus of the ellipse.

2. During a fixed amount of time, an imaginary line joining a planet to the Sun would trace out the same area. Consequently a planet travels more quickly when it is closer to the Sun.

Kepler's model gave more accurate predictions of planetary motions. It differed from the Copernican model in three important ways: the orbit is elliptical not circular; the Sun isn't at the centre of the orbit; and the planet's speed isn't constant.

Seeing other worlds

In 1608 in Holland, just before the publication of Kepler's book, the telescope was invented, changing astronomy forever. The identity of its inventor is uncertain, but the credit usually goes to the Dutch lens-maker Hans Lippershey who applied to patent his arrangement of two lenses for the magnification of distant objects by a factor three. Whether or not Lippershey actually invented the telescope, the scientific genius Galileo Galilei heard of it in 1609 and made his own improved version in a matter of days.

Most importantly, Galileo had the idea of turning his more powerful telescope towards the heavens. It's impossible to overestimate or even imagine the impact this invention must have had. Through it, Galileo could view the Moon and see it had its own landscape. He looked at the planets and saw that they were other worlds, not just points of light like the stars. He even saw moons around Jupiter.

The more Galileo saw and thought, the more convinced he became that the Copernican/Keplerian model of the heavens was correct. He recognized that the planets

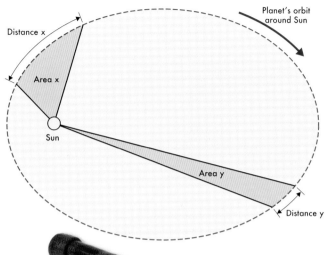

Distance x

Area x

Sun

Planet's orbit around Sun

Area y

Distance y

Kepler's second law describes the speed of a planet moving in an elliptical orbit around the Sun. The diagram shows that a line between the Sun and the planet sweeps equal areas in equal times. The planet's speed increases as it nears the Sun and decreases as it moves away from the Sun.

are other worlds, like our own, perhaps, and move around the Sun as Earth does. The Church had tolerated the Copernican model while it was not promoted as the truth, but it lost patience when Galileo wrote a letter stating that the Earth definitely orbits the Sun and, most controversially, that the Bible shouldn't be taken literally. His letter, written in 1613, was forwarded to the Inquisition in 1615, and in 1616 the Church banned the teaching of the Copernican model, withdrew Copernicus' book and instructed Galileo to stop promoting his belief.

However, in 1632, Galileo published his *Dialogue Concerning the Two Chief World Systems, Ptolemaic and Copernican*, which promoted the Copernican model. Even though he claimed that the model was only hypothetical, he was convicted of heresy in 1633. To avoid execution, he recanted his 'abjured, cursed and detested' findings and spent the last nine years of his life

Below: *One of Galileo's first telescopes.*

under house arrest. His book was finally removed from the register of banned books in 1757, but the Church didn't publicly admit that Galileo had been wrongfully condemned until 1992.

'Galileo, who practically invented the experimental method, understood why only the Sun could function as the centre of the world, as it was then known, that is to say, as a planetary system. The error of the theologians of the time, when they maintained the centrality of the Earth, was to think that our understanding of the physical world's structure was, in some way, imposed by the literal sense of Sacred Scripture.'

Pope John Paul II, 1992

Thinking about origins

In 1632, French philosopher René Descartes devised a theory about how the solar system formed. The idea that it had been created by some physical means which could be investigated scientifically would have been considered heretical, and Descartes judiciously kept his ideas to himself. Although he wrote his book in 1632 or 1633, it wasn't published until 1664, fourteen years after his death.

Swirling matter

Descartes proposed that the universe (not just the solar system) is filled with swirling vortices of particles. As he didn't believe a vacuum could exist, he reasoned that the vortices pressed right up against one another

and were packed with matter. Clearly, if matter was to be in motion and there was no empty space to move into, the only possible motion was circular. This movement was initiated, in Descartes' system, by God putting it all in motion.

Within each vortex, matter formed bands that were fixed. In our vortex, the solar system, the Sun lay at the centre. Each planet was stationary within a band, though the bands themselves turned around the centre of the vortex, each at a different speed. This meant the Earth was stationary in relation to its band, with the band carrying it along (just as a person is stationary in a moving train). This model allowed Descartes to claim to be observing the Church's diktat that the Earth doesn't move

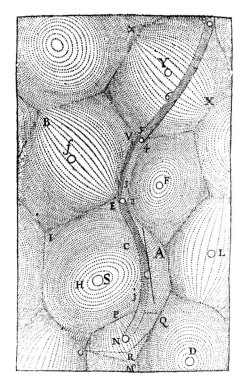

'The Earth, properly speaking, is not moved, nor are any of the Planets; although they are carried along by the heaven.'
René Descartes, 1644

Descartes' system of vortices had matter moving in spherical clouds, packed closely against one another.

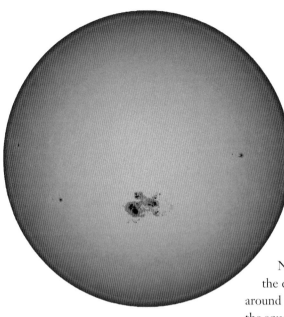

Descartes thought sunspots were the result of a build-up of matter out of place in the solar system's vortex.

Of planets and onions

Descartes also allowed matter to move outside its original vortex; this, he argued, would explain the formation of planets. Within each vortex, he maintained, matter tends to flow from the poles towards the equator. Normally, primary matter moves from the centre (the Sun), out at the poles and around the vortex vertically, re-entering at the equator. At the equator – the widest point of the vortex – adjacent vortices push against one another. Routinely, neither encroaches on the other's territory.

But things can go wrong in Descartes' model. The central star is made of primary matter, but if excessive secondary or tertiary matter builds up on its surface it can prevent the flow of primary matter back in at the equator. In our solar system Descartes believed we see this build-up as dark sunspots. Matter continues to flow from the poles and also now emerges at the equator, emptying the core and destroying the outward pressure that keeps the system in equilibrium. The adjacent vortices are therefore no longer held at bay and the blighted vortex collapses under external pressure. The lump of exhausted star at the centre, encrusted with sunspot material, becomes a planet or comet which is adopted into a band of one of the vortices that has taken over its space.

while also using the Copernican model of the Earth revolving around the Sun – he was able both to have his cosmological cake and eat it.

Descartes distinguished three grades of matter within the bands. Large bodies such as planets and comets he called tertiary matter, atom-sized globules were secondary matter, and 'indefinitely small' bits of debris made up primary matter. Using these three categories he sought to explain all physical properties and movement, as follows. A planet or comet will come to rest in a band when the energy with which it is fleeing the centre of the vortex (its centrifugal force) is balanced by the centrifugal force of the smaller grades of matter. If it has greater centrifugal force than the matter in the band, it will carry on travelling outwards until it meets a band where equilibrium can be reached. Descartes accounted for gravity by the same method.

Descartes' theory of the formation of heavenly bodies from collapsing matter was particularly prescient, even if he got the mechanics and reasoning wrong. It failed as a model because neither Descartes nor his followers could make the mathematics work to support it.

Starting with nebulae

The first person to suggest a thesis which approaches our idea of a system condensing from a cloud (nebular hypothesis) was Emanuel Swedenborg in 1734. Swedenborg asserted that there was a 'first natural point' – a moment of contact between the physical and non-physical worlds. This first natural point is not entirely material, but the material universe comes from it.

In Swedenborg's model of the solar system, the Sun is matter in motion, the centre of a vortex. It's composed of the 'first element', the most refined., and surrounded by matter of the 'second element', which rotates around the Sun. Through compression, the second-element particles become coarser and form a kind of shell around it. Under centrifugal force, this slowly moves further away from the Sun, becoming like 'a belt or broad circle'. Eventually it is so stretched that it breaks into chunks. Larger chunks form into planets; smaller chunks fall back towards the Sun and become 'erratic bodies straying around the sun, such as we are accustomed to call solar spots'. Some planetary material leaves the solar system entirely to become new stars. Importantly, Swedenborg believed this mechanism related not just to the solar system but to other stars and planetary systems: 'in every world-system, the principles are the same.'

God and chaos

In his *General History of the Earth and the Theory of the Heavens*, published anonymously in 1755, Immanuel Kant developed a more recognizable nebular theory. Today Kant is more famous as a philosopher than a physicist, but in the 18th century, when scientists

An illustration from Louis Figuier's The World Before the Deluge, *1897, showing the proto-Earth forming from a gassy nebula in space.*

went by the name of 'natural philosophers', there was little distinction between the intellectual realms. Kant drew on Newton's theory of universal gravitation and on the work of other scientists to attempt to explain the formation of the universe in a coherent scientific model.

Kant didn't dispense with God as Creator, but gave the Deity a very necessary role in designing the physical laws by which the universe was made and operates. He went on to suggest that originally there was a state of chaos in which all the matter that would eventually form stars, planets and other bodies was distributed, unconnected and unformed, in clouds. Immediately, lighter material started to move towards the heavier material as Newton's work on gravity dictates. Over

The German scientist-philosopher Immanuel Kant.

time, this process created our Sun (or another similar star), leaving a region of empty space which it had once occupied. Other accumulations of heavier matter were initially attracted to and then repulsed by the central body. They, too, attracted lighter matter from the space around them; this process resulted in the formation of planets. The planets moved around the star, the size of their orbit determined by the original attractive force. Again, their orbit was devoid of other matter as the planets had drawn it into themselves. The result was a group of planets in stable orbits through empty space around a large, dense star. Moons formed around planets in much the same way. Kant also suggested that there were several planets beyond Saturn (not then known); these accounted for the increasing eccentricity of the orbits of the known planets because they lay further from the Sun.

COMETS GET IN ON THE ACT

In 1745, French scientist Georges Leclerc, Comte de Buffon, proposed a rather different way that the planets could have formed. He suggested a comet had crashed into the Sun and the force of the impact had broken off chunks which were thrown out into space. When the force with which they were ejected was balanced by the gravitational pull of the Sun, they fell into orbit and became the planets. Leclerc was not overly concerned with the possibility of other planetary systems, so didn't need to address the chance of every star being hit by a comet with sufficient force to break off planetary material. Nor did he worry too much about the source of the comets.

Visualization of a proto-solar system forming in Laplace's nebular model. The whirling cloud of gas solidifies into planets.

Chilling in space

In 1796, Laplace described a nebular scenario in which the Sun originally had an extensive diffuse atmosphere that spread across the entire solar system. As it cooled, it contracted, eventually throwing out material which became the planets.

Laplace's model was popular, but had inherent problems, one being that the distribution of angular momentum between the Sun and the planets did not match his predictions. Later in the 19th century, James Clerk Maxwell (1831–79) pointed out that the different velocities of material travelling in the inner and outer parts of a ring would not allow the condensation of matter in the way Laplace had proposed. By the beginning of the 20th century, Laplace's theory had fallen out of favour, but there was no compelling alternative.

Out in the cold

In 1969, Soviet scientist Victor Safronov laid the groundwork for modern nebular theory. Although space travel had begun at this point, it was not yet yielding much information about the ingredients of the solar system. With little hard information to draw on, Safranov's work was largely theoretical. In the midst of the Cold War, Soviet scientists were developing their ideas separately from the cosmologists in the West, and took a decidedly different and apparently correct turn. Safronov began by assuming that the material which eventually became the planets was made up of dust, gas and grains of ice orbiting the Sun in a disk-shaped cloud. He realized that the orbits would be elliptical and he calculated the speed at which particles would collide as their orbits crossed. He found that those travelling at high speeds in relation to one another would be disrupted, but those travelling more slowly would stick together, making a larger lump. Over time, the lump would be of sufficient mass for its gravity to attract more particles and it would grow even larger.

With the passing of millions of years, the disk would become a collection of planetesimals orbiting in space that had largely been cleared of smaller particles. Safronov realized that the nature of the particle collisions would mean the planets had (at least initially) similar axial tilts. Although it took a while to be accepted, his work now forms the basis of the widely accepted solar nebular disk model (SNDM) and has been augmented by sophisticated computer models of early particle interactions and by Hubble images of evolving planets and protoplanetary disks.

The Kyoto model

The so-called Kyoto model, developed by Chushiro Hayashi in the 1970s, built on Safronov's explanation, stressing the importance of gas in the disk. Its effect would be to produce drag, slowing down the solid particles of dust; it would also allow the formation of the gas planets, a process that was not well explained by Safronov's model alone.

The sequence of planetary formation from a disk of gas and dust. Gaps appear in the disk as planets form over around 10 million years and clear their orbits of debris. More matter is swept up, and blown out into space by solar winds and radiation. After around 1 billion years, just a thin disk of debris remains around the planetary system.

An artist's impression of 'space snow' around V883 Orionis, 1,350 light years from the solar system.

The formation of our solar system is revealed by the composition of its planets, asteroids and other bodies. In the last half century, space probes have returned detailed information about (and even samples of) matter from elsewhere in the solar system.

Whether planets form as gas giants, ice giants or rock depends on the distance from their star. Astronomers define a snowline, or frostline, as a point in the protoplanetary disk where water freezes and circulates as ice rather than gas. Outside this line, gas giants can form. Closer to the star the only solid particles are dust (typically iron and other debris from previously destroyed systems); this leads to the formation of denser planets closer to the star.

In 2016, the Atacama Large Millimeter/submillimeter Array (ALMA), situated in the Chilean Andes took the first photo of a defined snowline around the young star V883 Orionis, in the constellation of Orion. Typically we would expect the snowline to be situated around 3 AU (450 million km/280 million miles) from the star, but an increase in the brightness of V883 Orionis has pushed its snowline back to about 40 AU (6 billion km/3.7 billion miles). This makes it visible. The snowline in our own solar system lies between the orbits of Mars and Jupiter.

Origins beyond Earth

By the time the Kyoto model was in circulation, astronomy had changed again. Now, instead of thinking only in terms of our own solar system, astronomers were beginning to discover evidence of worlds existing outside of it.

A heretical idea

The idea of other worlds was first posited in Greece, about 2,500 years ago. The Ancient Greeks differentiated the planets as specks of light which were distinct from the stars because they moved and didn't twinkle. In his *Letter to Herodotus*, the philosopher Epicurus (*c*.341–27 BC) wrote: 'There is an infinite number of worlds, some like this world, others unlike it. For the atoms being infinite in number . . . out of which a world might arise, or by which a world might be formed, have not all been expended on one world or a finite number of worlds, whether like or unlike this one. Hence there will be nothing to hinder an infinity of worlds.'

A natural extension of Epicurus' belief in an infinite number of atoms was that

The prolific Greek philosopher Epicurus wrote around 300 treatises on various subjects.

'He posits many worlds, many suns, necessarily containing similar things in kind and in species as in this world, and even men.'
From the trial of Giordano Bruno, executed for heresy in 1600.

there must be more worlds to accommodate them, as this world clearly could not. Epicurus was not alone in his view. The early atomist Democritus had considered the possibility of other worlds in the 5th century BC: 'In some worlds there is no Sun and Moon, in others they are larger than in our world, and in others more numerous. In some parts there are more worlds, in others fewer... in some parts they are arising, in others failing. There are some worlds devoid of living creatures or plants or any moisture.' Despite this, Aristotle's view prevailed: 'There cannot be more worlds than one.'

In 1686, French author Bernard le Bovier de Fontenelle published *Conversations on the Plurality of Worlds*, which explained to a general audience the Copernican model of the solar system, posited the idea of extraterrestrial life and suggested that the fixed stars are suns, each of which illuminates a world. In 1698, Christiaan Huygens' book *Cosmotheoros* was published posthumously; it suggests it is more reasonable to suppose that other planets have a variety of life than none at all, and as other stars are suns, that they too should have inhabited planets. Huygens made the perfectly logical (and accurate) assumption that the reason we cannot see the planets around other stars is that we are simply too far away.

By the 20th century, the belief that other stars might have planets was mainstream. In 1924, Edwin Hubble stated: 'The scientific community has long supposed that if stars are suns (and vice versa!), and the Sun has planets, then it is highly probable that the other stars also have planets.'

Exoplanets appearing

It seems that Huygens had looked unsuccessfully for exoplanets in the 17th century. The first dedicated search of this kind focused on Barnard's star in the mid-20th century. Dutch astronomer Peter van de Kamp spent many years examining

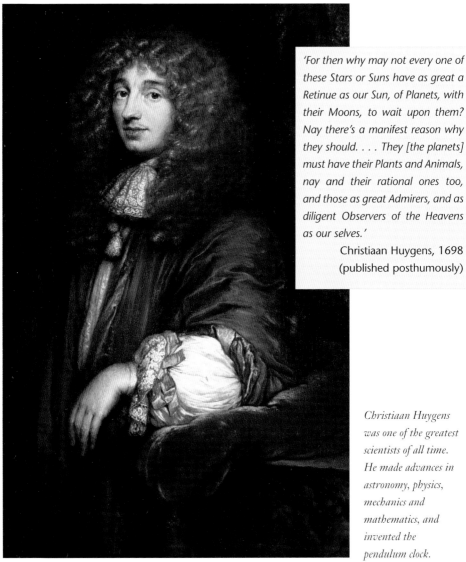

'For then why may not every one of these Stars or Suns have as great a Retinue as our Sun, of Planets, with their Moons, to wait upon them? Nay there's a manifest reason why they should. . . . They [the planets] must have their Plants and Animals, nay and their rational ones too, and those as great Admirers, and as diligent Observers of the Heavens as our selves.'

Christiaan Huygens, 1698 (published posthumously)

Christiaan Huygens was one of the greatest scientists of all time. He made advances in astronomy, physics, mechanics and mathematics, and invented the pendulum clock.

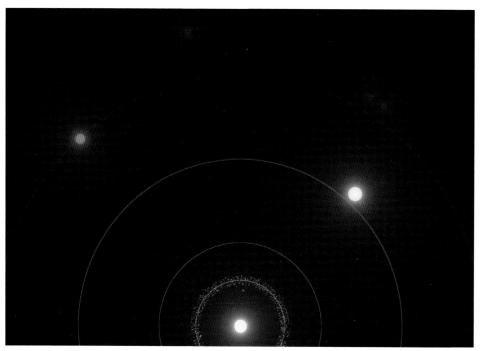

Barnard's star (the red orb on the left) is the second-closest star to the Sun; the closest, Alpha Centauri (the yellow and red orbs on the right) is a three-star system.

photographs of Barnard's star and found a wobble he calculated could be explained by the presence of a planet with 1.6 times the mass of Jupiter. He updated his claim in 1982 to two separate planets with masses 0.7 and 0.5 times that of Jupiter. Later astronomers have failed to reproduce his findings and it seems that they were invalid, but other exoplanets soon appeared out of the darkness. Since the first exoplanet was discovered in 1995, astronomers have found around 4,000 planets orbiting other stars in the Milky Way.

IT WAS THERE ALL ALONG

Although Peter van de Kamp was wrong when he 'found' either a super-Jupiter or two smaller planets around Barnard's star, astronomers believe there might now be a planet after all. Barnard's star is one of our near neighbours, just six light years from the Sun. It's a white dwarf, much smaller than the Sun, with only a tenth of its mass. The planet, if it's there, orbits the star at about the snowline, just outside the habitable zone (see page 172). Its year is 233 Earth days long, and its surface temperature might be as low as -150 °C (-238 °F). It is at least three times the mass of Earth and possibly much larger. In 2019, astronomers announced that the planet might have liquid subsurface oceans so could possibly host life, despite the frozen surface.

A general recipe for a solar system

The work of the last half century has yielded a model of planetary formation that should be relevant to other star systems:

• Within a million years of a star's formation, it will have a protoplanetary disk which consists of dust and gas particles.

• Gravity will cause the dust to clump together, producing lumps around 1 cm (0.39 in) in diameter over a period of a thousand years or so.

• As long as the density of particles is high enough, accretion enters a runaway phase where clumps collide and either join or disperse, only to be absorbed by other growing clumps.

• As the number of clumps reduces, growth slows and there is a phase of 'oligarchic accretion' where larger planet embryos absorb smaller ones.

• Within 10 million years, the protoplanetary disk has been used up (accreted by the star or emerging planets or evaporated or expelled into space). The area it once filled is occupied instead by clumps of matter orbiting in empty space.

• In the inner regions of a planetary system, a number of large planet embryos will combine to form planets approximately the size of Earth.

• Further out, planets accrete around ice and gather up gas. They can become much larger than those closer to the star.

Most of the system is understood, though how clumps of matter grow from 1 cm to 1 km is still uncertain. The answer to this might also explain why some stars never form planets (if, indeed, this is the case).

The snowline will determine whether a planet forms as a rocky (terrestrial) planet or a gas/ice planet. Gas planets can grow to ten times the size of terrestrial planets.

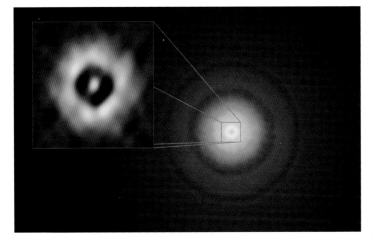

The planet-forming disk around the young Sun-like star T Hydrae. The inset image zooms in on the planetary gap nearest the star, about the same distance from it as Earth is from the Sun. Other gaps show where planets are forming further out.

GREAT BALLS OF GAS

The gas and ice giants in our solar system account for nearly 99 per cent of the mass of matter orbiting the Sun. The ice that forms embryonic gas planets is far more abundant than the heavy metals and minerals that form the rocky planets, which means a solar system can make more – and bigger – gas planets than rocky planets.

Growth leads to even greater growth. Once an embryonic planet has reached a certain size, it has enough mass to capture even the elements hydrogen and helium which are too light for the smaller planets to hold on to. The gases make an envelope around the embryonic planet, which grows ever more quickly especially once the mass of the envelope is the same as the mass of the core. Jupiter probably grew to 150 times the mass of the Earth in 100,000 years. Saturn is a lot smaller than Jupiter – probably because it formed a few million years later and Jupiter had already used up much of the planet-making material.

Barnard's galaxy, 1.6 million light years away, has many star-forming areas.

177

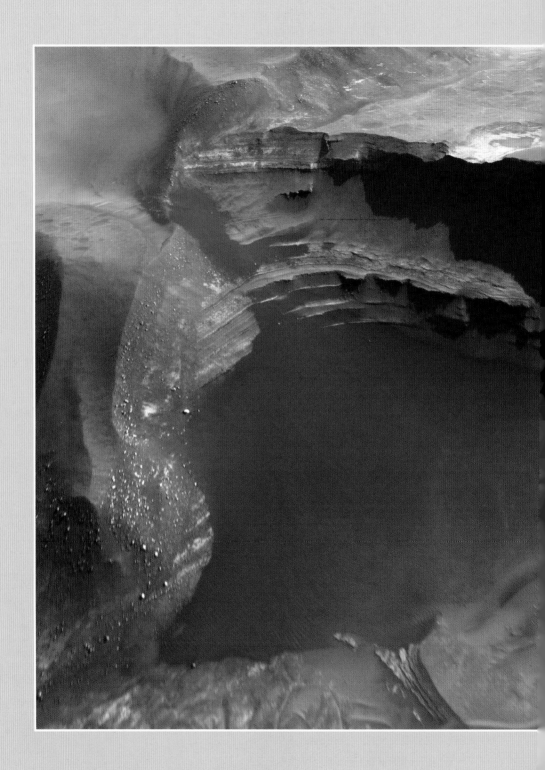

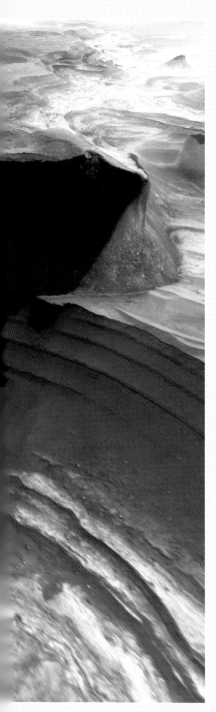

HOMING IN ON HOME

'We say that there is indeed likeness between all stars, between all worlds, and that our own and the other earths are similarly organized.'

Giordano Bruno,
On the Infinite Universe and Worlds
(Fourth Dialogue)

Planets come in all shapes and sizes, from rocky bodies smaller than Earth, through gas and ice giants, to potential 'super-Earths' and 'super-Jupiters' around other stars. We are only just beginning to discover their potential variety and find out exactly how these planets might have formed.

A three-dimensional visualization of flying over the surface of Mars, made from data collected by the Mars Orbiter.

A computer-generated view of the land around volcano Sapas Mons on the surface of Venus. The volcano is 400 km (248 miles) across and solidified lava flows surround it.

Planets growing up

When our own star formed from its collapsing cloud of gas and dust 4.6 billion years ago, 99.9 per cent of the material fell to the centre of the cloud to make the Sun. The final tenth of a per cent became the protoplanetary disk and gave rise to all the planets, moons, asteroids and comets that now orbit the Sun.

Our solar system has a band of rocky planets (Mercury, Venus, Earth and Mars) followed by a band of gaseous and icy planets (Saturn, Jupiter, Uranus and Neptune). In between is a band of asteroids which are generally considered to be debris left over from planet building and collisions. The rocky planets all have a metal core, rich in iron. There are two main theories to account for the formation of planets: the core accretion model, and the disk instability model.

The core accretion model

Gravity keeps the heaviest materials nearest to a star, so rocky planets form closest to the centre of a solar system. The heaviest materials, heavy metals, are drawn to the middle of each accreting planet. Silicate rocks gather around the metal-rich core, first forming a thick layer of gooey semi-molten rock. Eventually, the top of this hardens into the planet's solid crust.

While rocky planets are still molten, any newly arriving heavier material is likely to be dragged by gravity towards the centre and added to the core. Once a planet has achieved a certain mass, its increased gravity enables it to acquire and hold on to lighter materials. It can build a layer of gases around it – an atmosphere.

Mercury, the smallest of the four rocky planets, has very little atmosphere. It has the least mass of the four and is so close

ROCKS FROM MARS

We have not yet collected samples of rock directly from another rocky planet and returned them to Earth, though some missions have collected and examined rocks in situ. We do, however, have plenty of samples of Mars rock that have arrived on Earth as meteorites. These lumps of basaltic rock have been blasted out of the surface of Mars by asteroid impacts and hurled into space. After, typically, a few million years in orbit they have been pulled in by Earth's gravity and crashed to the ground where we can collect them to learn about the composition of another rocky planet. The provenance of the meteors has been ascertained by comparing the composition of tiny bubbles of gas trapped within them with the atmosphere of Mars, as tested by the *Viking* landers in 1976.

A piece of meteorite from Mars, two billion years old.

to the Sun that any atmosphere is readily ripped away by the solar wind. Venus and Earth both have substantial atmospheres, although that of Venus is composed mainly of carbon dioxide and is much denser and hotter than that of Earth.

The disk instability model

The core accretion model doesn't account well for the formation of the gas and ice giants. The process of building a large core would take too long, millions of years, by which time the gases needed for the huge atmosphere would have been driven out of the solar system. The disk instability model

suggests instead that clouds of gas and dust clump together in the protoplanetary disk. As these clumps cool and contract, heavier material groups together and gravitates to the centre to form a core. As the mass of a clump grows, it can attract more and more matter, much of which will be gas. The result is a solid core, a bit like a proto-rocky planet, with a giant cocoon of gas around it.

There's no reason to suppose that only one method of planet building exists. The variety of planets found around other stars (see page 154) suggests that planets can be made in several different ways.

GAS AND ICE GIANTS

The gas giants of our solar system are less dense than Earth but have much greater mass: Jupiter has 300 times and Saturn 95 times Earth's mass. They have a small, solid core, surrounded by gases (mostly hydrogen and helium) in different states according to the gases' density. Close to the core, hydrogen is liquid, but further from the core it is a gas, though under great pressure.

The ice giants Uranus and Neptune are at least ten times the mass of Earth. Built mostly of compounds that existed as ice at the time of their formation and probably made of carbon, nitrogen, oxygen and sulphur, they have much less hydrogen and helium than the gas giants. Around a small rocky core they have a hot, dense slurry of ice made largely of water, methane and ammonia (despite being hot, the pressure forces the molecules so close together that they form a semi-solid, icy sludge). There is a gaseous atmosphere beyond the thick layer of icy material.

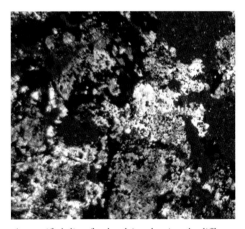

A magnified slice of a chondrite, showing the different grains present.

The raw material of planets

Luckily for science, not all the material of the protoplanetary disk of the Sun was swept up into planets and moons. There was plenty left over which became asteroids and meteors. Sometimes these fall to Earth, and we have learned about the matter circling our Sun 4.55 billion years ago from these invaluable samples. Stony meteorites, also called chondrites, are solidified chunks of protoplanetary disk, the most fundamental building blocks of the solar system. Although many have suffered shocks (including collisions and radioactive decay) that have heated and partially melted them, changing their structure, others remain pristine.

Stardust captured

Chondrites contain near-spherical tiny globules of silicate minerals and metal called chondrules. These were once free-floating molten droplets in the protoplanetary disk, but have become trapped in a matrix of dust. The dust includes presolar grains, tiny specks which predate the solar system and come from previous generations of stars.

We can see the history of the universe in the presolar grains of chondrites. They have chemical and structural fingerprints that can be matched to particular types of events in stars. If we knew enough, we could trace the origin of every grain to its parent star and see how a meteorite has been forged from the dust of multiple stars scattered throughout the galaxy.

The grains were the solid dust in the gas that condensed in the protoplanetary disk, and around which matter accreted. Many have been absorbed in planets and other large bodies and are effectively lost to us.

Presolar grains represent only a fraction of a per cent of the mass of chondrites. Within them, the ratio of isotopes of two rare gases, neon and xenon, differs from the standard ratios in the solar system. This difference is the clue to their origins.

Stardust signatures

In the 1960s, the prevailing belief was that the gas cloud which condensed to form the solar system was entirely homogenous. When mass spectroscopy revealed the different isotopic ratios of the noble gases in some primitive meteorites, people initially tried to explain the variations according to the existing model.

This only changed in the 1970s when American astrophysicist Donald Clayton proposed that supernovae events are immensely radioactive and produce many radioisotopes (see page 184). Clayton calculated the prevalence of isotopes produced by supernovae and released into the interstellar medium. Some of these isotopes then decay into others; Clayton worked out what the ratios of different isotopes should be in the interstellar medium. He successfully linked the composition of presolar grains to the activity of long-dead stars, introducing stardust to the examination of chondrites.

Donald Clayton, left, with William Fowler (see page 138).

GRITTY EVIDENCE

Some presolar grains from supernovae contain large quantities of the calcium isotope Ca-44. In the solar system generally, the proportion of calcium that is Ca-44 is only two per cent. Clayton found that the excess Ca-44 is the remains (the radioactive decay product) of titanium-44, which is produced in large quantities in Type II supernovae. But Ti-44 has a half-life of only 59 years, so not much of it will be left after 4.6 billion years. The product of its decay, Ca-44, is stable, so it will not go away. Finding Ca-44 in a presolar grain reveals that the grain came from a Type II supernova.

In 1975, Clayton proposed that condensed bits of matter from red giants and supernovae – stardust, in other words – would exist throughout the interstellar medium and could explain the anomalous ratios of isotopes. His suggestion was ignored; at this point, even the existence of stardust was purely hypothetical. In 1987, improved mass spectroscopy revealed residues from chondrites that matched the isotopic ratios Clayton had predicted for a certain type of red giant star. He was vindicated, and the discovery of stardust is officially dated at 1987.

Making comets

Comets are formed from dust and ice in the outer reaches of the solar system, well beyond Pluto. NASA's Stardust mission collected dust from the comet Wild 2 in 2004 and returned it to Earth. It was expected that Stardust would return a mix of ice and presolar grains, but there were

very few of the latter. Most of the comet consisted of ice and rock from within the solar system. The rock was in the form of chondrites and a few particles known as Calcium Aluminum Inclusions (CAIs). The chondrites, like those in meteors, had melted at incredibly high – white-hot – temperatures near the Sun in the early days of the solar system; they had then condensed. Somehow the chondrites had been hurled to the edge of the solar system where they had merged with ice to form comets. This unexpected result has

The comet Wild 2 photographed by NASA's Stardust spacecraft in 2004.

implications for how materials have been distributed throughout the solar system.

Rocks in space

The asteroids in the solar system lie mostly in a belt between Mars and Jupiter. When Jupiter formed, its gravity prevented the formation of more planets in this region. The asteroid belt contains debris from objects that have collided and smashed and never been incorporated into a planet. It includes up to 1.9 million asteroids which are at least 1 km (0.6 miles) across. Ten thousand near-Earth asteroids are known, of which 1,409 are classified as potentially hazardous, meaning that they could pose a threat to Earth. Collisions between orbiting bodies can be catastrophic: an asteroid or comet striking Earth near the Gulf of Mexico probably caused the extinction event 66 million years ago which killed the non-avian dinosaurs and many other species. The possibility of this had already occurred to Pierre-Simon Laplace in 1797, even before any mass extinctions were known.

'The small probability of collision of the Earth and a comet can become very great . . . over a long sequence of centuries. It is easy to picture the effects of this impact on the Earth. The axis and the motion of rotation have changed, the seas abandoning their old position . . . a large part of men and animals drowned in this universal deluge, or destroyed by the violent tremor imparted to the terrestrial globe.'

Pierre-Simon Laplace, 1796

An artist's concept of an asteroid belt.

The far side of the Moon is more cratered than the nearside, bearing the scars of many impacts.

High impact

In the early days of the solar system, collisions between asteroids and the newly formed planets were common. From 4.1 to 3.8 billion years ago, a period known as Late Heavy Bombardment saw the planets pummelled by asteroids and comets. Evidence of this is visible as scars and craters on the Moon and on Mercury. To see just how many asteroids might have slammed into Earth, we need only look at the far side of the Moon. Its surface is pitted with craters, and craters within the craters, which have been caused by countless impacts. Asteroids undoubtedly contributed to the geology of Earth, but there is no evidence of the bombardment because weathering and geological activity have removed all trace.

Gold from the sky

Even though iron and heavier elements such as gold were drawn to Earth's core when it was formed, today we can mine these elements near the surface of our planet. The best explanation for this, suggested in the 1970s, is that most of Earth's accessible heavy and precious metals were delivered by meteorites. Around 200 million years after Earth formed, it began to be bombarded by rocks from space. An estimated 20 billion billion (quintillion) tonnes of asteroids rained down, bringing metals that were incorporated into the Earth's crust. The presence of gold in rock brought back from the Moon's surface seems to support this.

Another theory is that some of the heavy metals dissolved in the molten rock of the mantle but did not make it to the core. These were then brought back to the surface by volcanic activity. Even so, the proportions of different metals found at the Earth's surface still require meteorites to have delivered some of them.

A HEART OF GOLD?

Gold was not the only precious metal to sink to the core in the early days of Earth's formation. Other useful and valuable metals, including platinum, are also down there. It's believed that there is enough precious metal in Earth's core to cover its surface with a layer 4 m (13 ft) thick.

Making a moon

While many collisions with space rocks caused large dents on Earth's surface, one such event may have had a far more dramatic outcome. Very early in the solar system's history, about 100 million years after the Earth was formed, a planet or protoplanet about the size of Mars slammed into Earth with such force that the Moon was created from the debris. This widely accepted giant-impact hypothesis was not the first attempt to account for the Moon's existence.

Another idea, the fission theory, was first proposed by George Darwin (son of Charles)

in 1898. He suggested that a chunk of early molten Earth had been hurled into space by the centrifugal force of the young planet's rapid rotation, and this formed the Moon. Another idea was that the Earth had captured the Moon from elsewhere. A further theory proposed that Earth and Moon had formed together at the birth of the solar system, both accreting from the protoplanetary disk as a binary system.

Of these theories, the first was for a long time held to be the most likely. Once people could measure the composition of the Moon and examine the elements and isotopes present there, it became clear that its rocks match those found in Earth's mantle, though they contain less iron, the material of Earth's core. If Earth and Moon had formed side by side from the same material (the third theory), we would expect them to have the same composition, including the same amount of iron. The third theory is also ruled out by the angular momentum of the Earth–Moon system. If (as according to the second theory) the Earth had captured the Moon from elsewhere in the solar system, we wouldn't expect such a good match between the materials of Earth's mantle and the rocks of the Moon.

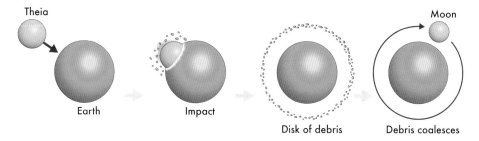

The formation of the Moon as a result of an impact from a Mars-sized planet, Theia.

Reginald Daly revisited Darwin's theory in 1945, but suggested that instead of Earth casting out a chunk of itself to become the Moon, another body had smashed into Earth and knocked out a chunk of it. This refinement went largely unnoticed until 1974, when it was revived and discussed by William Hartmann and Donald Davis and developed into the current giant-impact hypothesis.

This holds that an incoming planet, now named Theia, struck Earth at such an angle and with such force that Theia and a portion of the Earth were thrown out into space. Some of Theia, including its iron core, remained with the molten Earth and sank to become part of its core. Meanwhile a mix of debris from both planets went into orbit around Earth and coalesced into the Moon in a process that might have taken as little as a month or as long as a century. This explains reasonably well the relative composition of the Moon and Earth and the angular momentum of the Moon.

Turbulent innards

The result of this gigantic collision with Theia would have been a molten surface for both Earth and the Moon. Afterwards, Earth's surface would have slowly cooled and solidified, but the molten rock of the mantle continued, and continues, to flow slowly around the planet, carrying slabs of Earth's crust, called tectonic plates. Volcanic activity allows magma from the mantle out onto the surface, creating new rock. The same thing happened on the Moon initially, but it is no longer geologically active and its volcanoes are probably extinct. Other planets and moons in the solar system also have volcanoes, many of which erupt water or ice instead of molten rock. Geological activity seems to be a feature we can expect to find in other planetary systems.

Stuff from space

Asteroids, comets and meteors seem to have delivered materials found near the

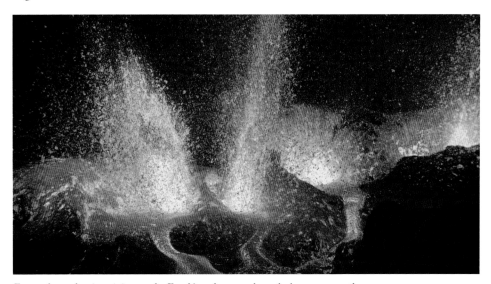

Even today, volcanic activity recycles Earth's rocky crust through the upper mantle.

The exoplanet Kepler 10b was the first confirmed rocky exoplanet in 2011. It's 20 times closer to its star than Mercury is to the Sun, giving it a scorching surface at about 1,370 °C (2,500 °F).

surface of many planets – not only heavy metals, but also water and perhaps even the building blocks of life. Deposits of frozen water near Mercury's poles might have been delivered by comets billions of years ago. As they are perpetually in shadow, the ice will never melt.

One of the other surprises delivered by the Stardust mission was the presence of an amino acid, glycine. Amino acids are the building blocks of proteins, which form the basis of all life. The Stardust mission, then, revealed that at least one prebiotic molecule was delivered to Earth on comets and, inevitably, has been delivered to other bodies in the solar system.

Far from here

In our solar system we have a relatively limited set of planets: rocky ones near the centre, gas giants further out, and ice giants beyond those. The exoplanets (planets around other stars) discovered so far include many gas giants, some far larger than those in our solar system, and some large rocky planets, hot gassy planets and possibly hot ice planets. There are probably many rocky planets about the same size as Earth, but they are very difficult to detect. Rocky planets larger than Earth are called 'Super-Earths'. One theory is that the largest of these rocky planets are the cores of enormous gas planets that have lost their gassy envelope.

Hot Jupiters are gas giants that orbit very close to their star so have a very short orbital period and a very high temperature. The first exoplanet discovered orbiting a star like the Sun was called 51 Pegasi. It's twenty times closer to its star than Earth is to the Sun and has an orbital period of just four days.

A planet the size of Neptune, but fourteen times closer to its star than Mercury is to the Sun, orbits a red dwarf 30 light years from Earth. It is a 'hot ice' planet, thought to be mostly water. Some of the water will be in exotic forms of ice created under pressure, and its atmosphere might be water vapour.

Little is known of planets like these, which we can only just identify from far away. It's too early to say how they form or even exactly what they are like.

What about life?

We don't know whether life is common or rare in the universe, or even if Earth is unique as the only planet that supports it (which seems unlikely). Life might have started on Earth just a few hundred million years after the planet had formed.

From there to here

We know that life on Earth started at least 3.5 billion (possibly 4.3 billion) years ago. Photosynthesis, the process which now feeds the world, began at least 2.3 billion years ago. The method by which plants produce glucose from carbon dioxide and water, photosynthesis uses the energy from sunlight to power the reaction. It first emerged in single-celled organisms called cyanobacteria, which are similar to modern red-green algae. The massive amount of oxygen this produced caused the first mass extinction event, killing off most of the other simple organisms which didn't need and couldn't tolerate oxygen.

Then came the evolution of new life forms which depended on oxygen and lived in the sea. For a long time they remained fairly simple, but around 540 million years ago there was a sudden explosion of diversity. After that, evolution snowballed. Some organisms left the sea and colonized the land; terrestrial plants and animals diversified.

In the Carboniferous Period, 359–299 million years ago, the land was covered with rich forest; amphibians and arthropods, including insects, were the dominant land animals. Then climate change led to reptiles taking over; with the evolution of eggs that could be laid out of water, animals roamed further inland. The last 300 million years have seen everything from the evolution of dinosaurs, birds and mammals to the rise of humankind. Humans have been around for, at most, two million years – a mere blink of an eye in geological time.

Life in space

It's impossible to extrapolate from a sample found on one planet whether life is likely to be discovered elsewhere. If life on Earth started within a short time of the surface stabilizing, it suggests that it is quite easy to kick-start and could be common throughout the universe. However, it took Earth more than four billion years to evolve from a

An artist's concept of a theorized exoplanet orbiting Beta Pictoris, 63 light years away. The planet has an eight-hour rotation period (day) and turns more quickly than any planet in our solar system.

sterile planet to one in which the land was teeming with sophisticated life. And it has almost taken Earth's entire history to reach the point where one species, humans, can venture beyond its home planet. Perhaps this means that the evolution of advanced life, and particularly of a technological species, is very difficult and will seldom occur; or maybe any planet with life will get there in the end. We simply can't say.

Within our solar system, we can be pretty sure that Earth is the only rocky planet with liquid oceans and large life forms. But there could be life on other planets (perhaps below the surface, perhaps very small) and there may be life on some of their moons. As for exoplanets, we have little idea of whether they can support any form of life. For now, Earth remains our only model of a habitable planet and the varied life forms that live here our only models of life. Different forms of life could exist elsewhere, including some we might not even recognize as life.

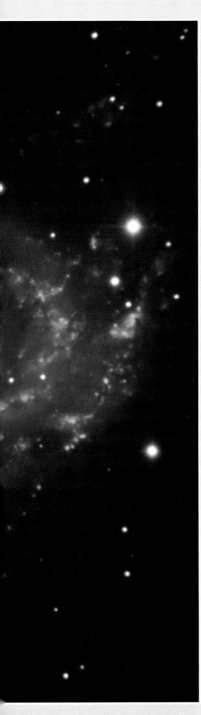

WHERE WILL IT ALL END?

*'In real time, the universe has a beginning
and an end at singularities that form a boundary
to space-time and at which the laws of science
break down.'*

Stephen Hawking,
*The Illustrated Theory of Everything:
The Origin and Fate of the Universe, 2003*

**The Big Bang theory gives us a pretty
good idea of how the universe started.
But how will it end? Three possible
scenarios dominate cosmological
thinking. Inevitably, none of them would
be good to live through, but fortunately
we won't be here to see it happen.**

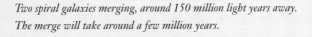

*Two spiral galaxies merging, around 150 million light years away.
The merge will take around a few million years.*

Bigger and bigger

As we have seen, the universe burst into life, went through a very brief period of exponential expansion, then settled into a pattern of steadily expanding. The impression is that it then set about a pattern of making and destroying stars, building planets and repeating this sequence, at each circuit enriching its building materials with elements made in the last round. But the universe had another surprise in store for astronomers. Around 5–6 billion years ago, the rate of expansion started to speed up. This was discovered as recently as 1998, and it overturned much of what we thought we knew.

The accepted model

For most of the 20th century, the cosmological model balanced the expansion of the universe against the force of gravity that pulls it together. It was expected that the rate of expansion would gradually slow and eventually stop altogether at some point in the distant future. But in 1998 the Hubble Space Telescope revealed that the rate of expansion of the universe has sped up rather than slowed down.

The rate at which the universe expands is known as Hubble's constant. It is stated in kilometres (or miles) per second per megaparsec (km/s/Mpc). Hubble first calculated the value of the constant in 1929, using Cepheid variable stars in the galaxy Andromeda. His figure of 342,000 miles per hour per million light years equates to around 500 km per second per megaparsec, which is nearly ten times the value currently accepted. It gave the universe an age of around two billion years. But there was almost immediately a problem with this figure. In the 1930s, radioactive dating established that there are three-billion-year-old rocks on Earth. How could Earth be older than the universe?

The first reasonably accurate estimate, 75 km/s/Mpc, was achieved in 1958 by

Panoramic photograph of the ESO's Very Large Telescope, the most advanced optical telescope in the world.

MEASURING HUBBLE'S CONSTANT

Today, cosmologists measure Hubble's constant by calculating the distance to two types of objects: Cepheid variable stars, and type Ia supernovae in distant galaxies. These both work as standard candles: they have stable and predictable luminosity. The rate at which a Cepheid variable star pulsates is an indication of its true brightness. By comparing this with its apparent brightness seen from Earth, astronomers can work out how far away it is. Type Ia supernovae explode with a standard brightness. By measuring the red shift of the light arriving at Earth, astronomers can work out a supernova's distance from Earth. The Hubble telescope has been used to calculate the distance to 2,400 Cepheid variable stars in 19 galaxies and 300 distant type Ia supernovae.

American astronomer Allan Sandage. A graduate student of Hubble's, Sandage produced data in 1952 that doubled the supposed age of the universe from 1.8 to 3.6 billion years, again working from Cepheid variable stars. A few years later, he increased the age to 5.5 billion years, and later to 20 billion years.

The first value calculated from the Hubble telescope observations was 72 ±8 km/s/Mpc in 2001. The most recent and accurate value from the telescope is 74.03 ±1.42 km/s/Mpc, made in 2019, but the most recent value calculated from the Planck measurement of the cosmic microwave background is 67.4 km/s/Mpc. The disparity is troubling. Cosmologists don't know the cause of the 'tension' (as they term it) between the figures, and the 2019 measurement increased the difference between them, throwing our physics into doubt. It could be that there is something wrong with our model of the cosmos, or some new type of unthought-of disruptive particle in the universe.

Edwin Hubble using a ground-based telescope.

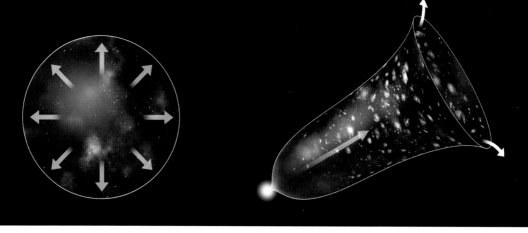

The cosmological constant acts as a force pushing the expansion of the universe outwards (left) resulting in a universe expanding ever more quickly over time (right).

Faster and faster

That the universe is still expanding matches the expectations we have of the Big Bang. But the fact that the rate of expansion is increasing rather than decreasing has dumbfounded cosmologists. In 2019, it was found to be increasing by as much as 9 per cent – even faster than previously thought. Data collected by the Hubble telescope looking at very distant supernovae shows that the universe expanded more slowly in the distant past. The search for an explanation has yielded three possibilities:

- the 'cosmological constant' which Einstein rejected on coming to accept the expansion of the universe should be reinstated

- some kind of energy-fluid fills space, pushing the galaxies further apart

- Einstein's theory of gravity is wrong and a new theory is needed.

Without being able to explain it, cosmologists have given a name to whatever drives the expansion – dark energy. This is not just a small component, it represents about 68 per cent of the matter/energy content of the universe.

Making more nothing

The prevailing theory is that dark energy pushes the galaxies further apart by creating more space between them. 'More space' can appear from nowhere. Einstein's equations show that space can simply come into existence. Further 'empty' space can possess energy. A consequence of putting these two together is that if more space appears, the energy density of space does not diminish. The more space that's added between galaxies, the more energy turns up to carry on pushing them further apart. The result would be what we have already seen – accelerating expansion – with the universe growing faster and faster as more and more space-with-energy appears between its parts. It's a neat solution, but it remains hypothetical.

As we have seen, quantum theory allows 'empty' space to harbour temporary or 'virtual' particles that appear and disappear rapidly with the result, again, that it's not really empty. It would seem at first that this might account for dark energy. But calculations using this idea come up with 10^{120} times too much energy. That's far more than we can get rid of by rejigging the calculations or tweaking the theory. The net result is that we simply don't know. Dark energy remains a great puzzle yet to be solved.

Where do we go from here?

Our ignorance about the nature of dark energy has a further important consequence – we don't know what will become of the universe in the future. If dark energy is a kind of field that turned on 5–6 billion years ago, might it also turn off at some point in the future? Or will it continue to fuel accelerating expansion forever?

Three broad possibilities for the future of the universe have been discussed. For thousands of years they have shaped and been reflected in myths and religions as well as philosophical discussions and, more recently, science:

- the universe could continue in perpetuity;

- it could come to an end, once and for all;

- it could end and restart in a great recycling project.

World without end

The same Ancient Greek philosophers who envisaged the universe with no beginning also supposed that it would have no end. An eternal universe stretches endlessly backwards and forwards in time. Newton was of the same opinion: the universe is eternal and, on the large scale, unchanging. Even Einstein agreed, adding his cosmological constant to compel a steady-state universe. But once the

discovery of cosmic microwave background radiation supported a specific moment of origin in the Big Bang, the future was cast into doubt.

Crunch or chill

By the late 20th century, cosmologists had come to agree on a universe finite in time, at least in its current form. They foresaw two possibilities for its ultimate fate. If there was enough matter in the universe, its gravity would eventually overcome the expansion and the universe would go into reverse. This contraction would accelerate as objects drew closer to one another, ending in a 'Big Crunch'. But if there wasn't enough matter to produce this much gravity, objects would drift further and further apart, losing heat and resulting in an infinitely dispersed, cold universe – the Big Chill or the heat death of the universe. In the early 1990s, calculations of the mass of the universe seemed to favour the Big Chill as its ultimate fate.

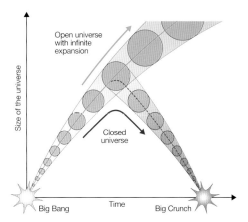

Two possible futures for the universe: eternally increasing size, or reversal and contraction, ending in a 'Big Crunch'.

QUINTESSENCE, OR AETHER

Aristotle suggested that a mysterious substance filled the celestial realms, which came to be known as 'quintessence'. Unlike the four classical elements believed to make up the Earth (earth, water, air and fire), quintessence was considered to be extremely refined or 'subtle', to move always in circles, to be unchanging, and to have none of the qualities of hot, cold, wet and dry that characterized the earthly elements. Later writers came to call this substance 'aether'. From the 1670s and Newton's work on light, a more modern version of aether emerged as a medium through which light and, later, other electromagnetic radiation could travel. Christiaan Huygens described waves of light travelling through an 'omnipresent, perfectly elastic medium having zero density, called aether'. In the 19th century, starting with the work of James Clerk Maxwell,

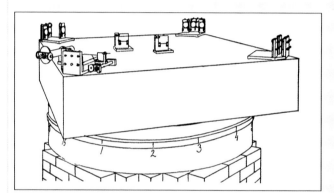

it became clear that aether was not actually needed to carry waves of energy through space. Albert Michelson and Edward Morley carried out a famous experiment to search for aether in 1887 but found no evidence of it. To date, no aether has been discovered.

Michelson and Morley's equipment was mounted on a stone slab over a pool of mercury. It compared the speed of light travelling in different directions, testing the difference between light travelling in the same direction as 'aether' and light travelling at right angles to it.

THE DEATH OF HEAT

The 'heat death' of the universe sounds as though it should be a hot termination, like the fiery cataclysms prophesied by some religions – but it's the opposite. In the 'heat death' of the universe, heat itself will die. The cooling of the universe was suggested by French astronomer Jean Sylvain Bailly in 1777. He believed that all planets have internal heat and slowly lose it over time. The Moon, he claimed, was already too cold to support life. Jupiter, on the other hand, was too hot to support life. Earth, clearly, is in a Goldilocks zone of being 'just right' – for now.

In 1852, Lord Kelvin outlined what would become the first two laws of thermodynamics and in 1862 wrote with reference to the Sun (see page 80) that energy is conserved, but mechanical energy is dissipated as heat. The result 'would inevitably be a state of universal rest and death', but only if the universe is finite. Kelvin believed it was 'impossible to conceive a limit to the extent of matter in the universe', therefore the universe could look forward to 'endless progress' rather than 'stopping forever'.

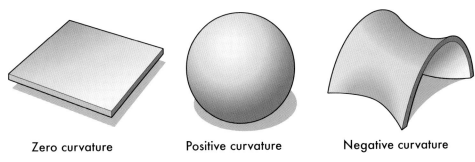

| Zero curvature | Positive curvature | Negative curvature |

Three possible shapes of the universe, represented in three dimensions.

New prospects

Everything changed in 1998 with the discovery that expansion is accelerating. The 'Big Rip' model proposes that runaway expansion will go much further than the heat-death of a Big Chill. Instead, dark energy could rip apart first galaxies and then stars, and eventually even molecules and atoms.

Today, astronomers tend to favour either the Big Chill or the Big Rip; the Big Crunch has fallen out of favour. Which it will be depends on the shape of the universe, the nature of dark energy and whether it continues to propagate or suddenly ceases to appear, perhaps as quickly as it apparently started to appear.

The shape of everything

There are three possible 'shapes' of the universe. It can have a positive curvature, negative curvature or no curvature at all. As it has three spatial dimensions and a time dimension, visualizing these states is virtually impossible, though they can be described mathematically. A flat surface needs no explanation. Positive curvature resembles the surface of a sphere and defines a closed universe. This type of universe has enough mass for gravity to stop expansion and eventually send it into reverse, leading to contraction and ultimately a Big Crunch. Negative curvature resembles a saddle-shape and defines an open universe. This universe has insufficient mass for gravity to overcome expansion and it will expand forever.

Most cosmologists think that the current set of data favours a flat universe. In this model there is just enough mass for expansion to slow to zero, but after an infinitely long time. This conclusion rests on data from the WMAP survey of the cosmic microwave background, which suggests that the universe is flat to within a margin of 0.4 per cent. It is, however, based on the observable universe; we can't know anything about the universe beyond the observable portion. It may look flat because we are seeing such a tiny part of the whole that its curvature is not apparent, just as we don't notice the curve of the Earth when we stand in a field and observe what we can of the world around us.

CHAPTER 9

Something from nothing

Cosmology has no terms or tools for addressing what might come after the end of the expansion of the universe, whether it takes the form of a Big Rip, Big Chill or Big Crunch. If there is a Big Crunch, perhaps it all begins over again, as some of the ancient mythical cosmologies – and some more recent cosmologists – suggest. If it ends with everything infinitely spread out, perhaps it will be an infinity of cold, dark nothingness. But it all started from nothing, and look what has come from that. If the story of the universe teaches us one thing, it's that 'nothing will come of nothing' is not a reliable dictum.

A bad day in the future: an artist's impression of the dying Sun, viewed from the surface of Earth, looking past the Moon.

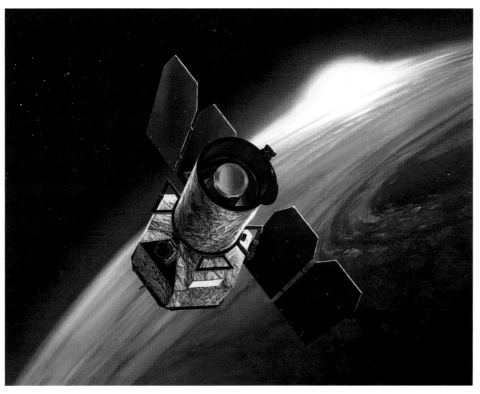

An artist's impression of the Galaxy Evolution Explorer launched in 2003 to study the stages of construction of galaxies that have evolved over the last 10 billion years.

THE END FOR US

There's no need to worry about the ultimate fate of the universe as our solar system will be gone long before then. The Sun, as a main sequence star about halfway through its life, will continue in much the same manner for another 5–6 billion years. Then, as it fuses the last of its hydrogen into helium, it will swell to around 250 times its current size. It will lose mass so its gravitational pull will reduce, enabling Earth to move further away from the ballooning red giant. Unfortunately, Earth's own gravity will create a tidal bulge on the Sun which will follow the Earth around in its orbit and eventually drag it to a fiery doom.

One crazy idea to save Earth and its inhabitants has been suggested – we could force objects from the Kuiper belt to become comets, passing by Earth closely enough to nudge its orbit. It would take about a million close encounters with objects 100 km wide (perhaps one every 6,000 years) to move Earth to a safer zone. It might be easier to move ourselves to a planet in a different solar system. After all, if we're still around in 5 billion years we'll have had 500,000 times as long as we've had since the start of civilization to come up with a sophisticated form of space travel.

INTO THE MULTIVERSE

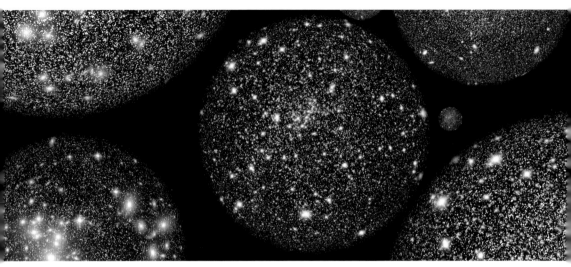

Multiverse theory posits a potentially infinite number of discrete bubble universes.

In this book we have focused on the story of the universe that is most widely accepted, but there are other versions. An inflationary model based on superstring theory and brane cosmology, developed by Paul Steinhardt and Neil Turok in 2002, suggests a universe that expands and contracts in cycles. String theory tries to tie together the four fundamental forces by envisaging particles as vibrating strings in an 11-dimensional universe.

Another model is of a multiverse – a collection of many, perhaps an infinite number, of universes of which ours is only one. The first 'many worlds' formulation was conceived by American physicist Hugh Everett in 1957; it was extended and popularized by Bryce DeWitt in the 1960s. It's a development of quantum theory and is an area of physics rather than cosmology. It proposes that all possible events have happened and will happen in different universes. Obviously this makes universes proliferate extremely rapidly. A different universe branches off every time you make a choice, and every time an ant does or does not climb a plant, or an asteroid does or does not hit a planet, or a radioactive atom does or does not decay, and so on.

An influential cosmological multiverse theory was first proposed by Russian-American physicist Andrei Linde in 1983. It is based on the idea that the cosmic inflation in the early universe didn't end after a fraction of a second but has continued and will continue for eternity. While we have no idea why inflation might have ended (so perhaps it didn't), this theory requires a complete re-think of the universe that followed the non-end of inflation.

In Linde's theory, our universe is one of many bubbles where inflation stopped or slowed because of conditions in the vacuum. Outside our universe are areas that are still expanding exponentially, together with many other 'bubble universes' that have slower expansion and, possibly, different laws of physics and dissimilar local conditions. More bubble universes break off all the time as expansion stops in particular locations.

Working with co-author Thomas Hertog, Stephen Hawking produced a counter-argument, published posthumously in 2018. This rested on the novel approach of dispensing with time and therefore with the 'moment' of the Big Bang. (Throwing out one dimension when manipulating theories is an accepted technique in physics, but it's usually a spatial dimension.) Because general relativity cannot be reconciled with the earliest nano-moment of the universe, we could dispense with the moment rather than the theory. Looking at inflation again in this new model, it all works tidily and produces a single, well-behaved universe. We might wonder, though, where time came from if it didn't start with the other dimensions at the Big Bang, or we might ask when it entered the equation. But, of course, 'when' isn't a meaningful word in a universe without time.

Knowing nothing about nothing

We began with a universe spawned from nothing. This was suggested at a time when people thought they knew, roughly, what the universe contains. We end with some explanation of the 'nothing', but a much less secure grasp of the 'something' it created. By current measures, only about 4 per cent of the universe is the normal matter and energy we are familiar with; that leaves 96 per cent as the inexplicable dark matter and dark energy.

There is plenty of work left for cosmologists to do. We are still a long way from understanding how the universe works.

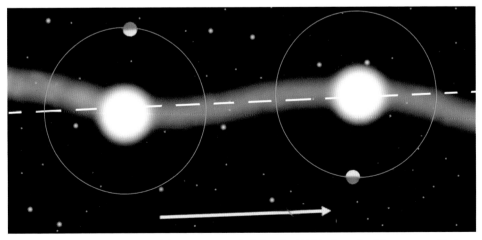

One way of detecting planets around distant stars is to look for a 'wobble' in the path of the star, caused by it being pulled towards its planet.

INDEX

PICTURE CREDITS

Alamy Stock Photo: 34 *left* (Science History Images), 34 *right* (Lebrecht Music & Arts), 52–3, 110 (Science History Images), 132 (FLHC 50), 146 (The Picture Art Collection)
AU Campus Emdrup, Copenhagen: 144
Bridgeman Images: 6 (Werner Forman Archive)
Brookhaven National Laboratory: 46, 47 *bottom*
CSIRO Australia: 66
Diomedia: 7 (Universal Images Group), 164, 169, 173
European Southern Observatory: *facing title page* and 19 *top*, 20 (PESSTO/S. Smartt), 23, 33, 95 *top* (Beletsky/DSS1 + DSS2 + 2MASS), 96 (M. Kornmesser), 115 *bottom*, 117, 120 (G. Beccari), 121, 123 *top* (NASA, ESA and the Hubble Heritage Team/STScI/AURA/F.Vogt *et al.*), 137 (ALMA/Hubble/NASA/ESA/CXC), 139, 143 (M. Kornmesser), 145 (Gravity Consortium/L. Calçada), 151 (M. Kornmesser), 154 (M. Kornmesser/Nick Risinger/skysurvey.org), 156 (H. Avenhaus et al./E. Sissa *et al.*/DARTT-S and SHINE collaborations), 172 (A. Angelich), 175 (IEEC/Science-Wave/Guillem Ramisa), 176 (S. Andrews/ALMA), 177, 178–9 (NASA/JPL/University of Arizona), 190–191 (L. Calçada/Nick Risinger/skysurvey.org), 192–3, 194–5 (G. Hüdepohl/atacamaphoto.com)
European Space Agency: 74 (ATG medialab), 77 (Hubble/NASA), 97 *top* (NASA/Hubble Heritage Team), 99 *top* (Hubble/NASA), 100 (NASA/A. Nota (STScI/ESA), 122, 149 (Hubble)
flickr.com/photos/torbenh/6105409913: 22
Getty Images: 10 (Corbis), 11 (De Agostini), 15 (Bettmann), 25 (The LIFE Images Collection), 35 (Science & Society Picture Library/Science Museum), 38 (Bettmann Archive), 40–41 (Dorling Kindersley RF), 58 (Science & Society Picture Library/Science Museum), 67 (The Print Collector), 70 (Science & Society Picture Library/Science Museum), 78, 82 (Archiv Gerstenberg/ullstein bild), 85 (Hulton Archive), 104 (Hulton Archive), 166 (Universal Images Group)
Harvard College Observatory: 111 *bottom*
Hubblesite: 8–9 (NASA, ESA and M. Montes/University of New South Wales)
NASA: 61 (WMAP Science Team), 62 (Goddard Space Flight Center/COBE Science Working Group), 63 (WMAP Science Team), 71 (JAXA), 72 (ESA/JPL-Caltech/Yale/CNRS), 76 (Desiree Stover), 88 (SDO/AIA), 92–3 (ESA/Hubble Heritage Team), 94 (GSFC/Dana Berry), 97 *bottom* (JPL-Caltech), 99 *bottom* (ESA/Hubble Heritage Team), 103 (NASA/CXC/M. Weiss), 116 (ESA/G. Bacon/STScI), 129 (CXC/NCSU/M. Burkey *et al.*), 130 (Tod Strohmayer/GSFC/CXC), 133 *left* (ESA/Hubble Heritage Team), 141 (NOAA/GOES Project), 152–3 (JPL), 157 (JHU's APL/SwRI), 158 (ESA/STScI), 165 *bottom*, 167 (SDO), 171, 180 (JPL), 181, 184 *top* (JPL-Caltech), 184–5, 189 (Kepler Mission/Dana Berry), 201 (JPL-Caltech)
Science Photo Library: 16 (Mark Garlick), 19 *bottom*, 27 (Emilio Segre Visual Archives/American Institute of Physics), 28 *top* (Mark Garlick), 39 (David Parker), 44 (Nicolle Rager Fuller/National Science Foundation), 45 (Andrew Lambert Photography), 50 (Emilio Segre Visual Archives/American Institute of Physics), 56 (Oxford Science Archive/Heritage Images), 57 (AIP/Emilio Segre Visual Archives), 73 (Los Alamos National Laboratory), 83 (N. A. Sharp, NOAO/NSO/Kitt Peak FTS/Aura/NSF), 108–9 (Emilio Segre Visual Archives/American Institute of Physics), 124–5 (NASA/Skyworks Digital), 126 (Frank Zullo), 128 (Historica Graphica Collection/Heritage Images), 135 *bottom* (Hencoup Enterprises), 155 (Royal Astronomical Society), 168 (Science Source), 170 (Chris Butler), 183 (Emilio Segre Visual Archives/American Institute of Physics), 186 (NASA), 196 (Mikkel Juul Jensen), 198 (Emilio Segre Visual Archives/American Institute of Physics), 200 (Chris Butler), 203 (Jon Lomberg)
Shutterstock: 12, 24, 28 *bottom*, 42, 47 *top*, 49, 59, 60, 80, 101, 105, 111 *top*, 182, 188
Spacetelescope.org: 17 *bottom*
SuperStock: 54, 68, 113 (Joseph Giacomin/Image Source), 148 (Classic Vision/age fotostock), 150 (mrk movie/Marka), 195 (Huntington Library), 202
Wellcome Collection: 133 *right*, 134, 135 *top*, 160, 163

Diagrams by David Woodroffe: 14, 21, 37, 43, 51, 55, 84, 89, 90, 91, 95 *bottom*, 102, 112, 114, 123 *bottom*, 136, 138, 140, 147, 159 *bottom*, 161, 165 *top*, 187, 197, 199